Health and Safety
Executive

Work equipment

Provision and Use of Work Equipment Regulations 1992

Guidance on Regulations
L22

London: HMSO

Enquiries regarding this or any other HSE
publication should be made to the HSE
Information Centre at the following address:

HSE Information Centre
Broad Lane
Sheffield S3 7HQ
Tel: (0742) 892345
Fax: (0742) 892333

Contents

Introduction

1   This publication gives general guidance on the Provision and Use of Work Equipment Regulations 1992, which come into force on 1 January 1993. The Regulations are reproduced in this publication, interspersed with relevant guidance.

2   The Regulations implement European Community (EC) Directive 89/655/EEC requiring similar basic laws throughout the EC on the use of work equipment at work.

3   The Regulations are made under the Health and Safety at Work etc Act 1974 (HSW Act), and apply to all employees and the self-employed covered by that Act in Great Britain except the crews of sea-going ships.

4   This guidance has been prepared by the Health and Safety Executive (HSE) for the Health and Safety Commission (HSC) after consultation with industry. It should not be regarded as an authoritative interpretation of the law and the presentation of the Regulations in this document does not constitute a Statutory Instrument. Unless otherwise stated the terms used in the guide can be taken to mean the same as those in the Regulations.

5   It is intended that the contents of this booklet should form a general framework within which industry associations and others will be able to produce more specific guidance appropriate to their own circumstances.

6   Employers should also take into account any relevant HSC/HSE publications giving guidance on other regulations, industries or equipment (see the reference section at the back of this guidance). Up-to-date information on these publications can be obtained from HSE's Information Centre.

Background

7   The Provision and Use of Work Equipment Regulations 1992 (PUWER) lay down important health and safety laws for the provision and use of work equipment. As explained in paragraph 11 and the guidance to regulation 1, the Regulations will take effect in two stages, some on 1 January 1993, others on 1 January 1997.

8   The primary objective of PUWER is to ensure the provision of safe work equipment and its safe use. This has several components which are interlinked and complementary. Work equipment should not give rise to risks to health and safety, irrespective of its age or place of origin.

9   The Regulations are set out as follows:

Regulations 1 to 3 deal with preliminary issues, ie date of entry into force of the Regulations, scope and limitations.

Regulation 4 defines who has duties, ie employers, persons in control and the self-employed.

Regulations 5 to 10 are general duties covering selection of suitable equipment, maintenance, information and instructions, training, etc.

Regulations 11 to 24 address the need for equipment to be able to control selected hazards, for example contact with dangerous parts of machinery, the risk of fire and explosion, disintegration, contact with hot and cold surfaces, instability, etc.

Regulations 25 to 27 deal with exemption certificates, extension outside Great Britain and repeals and revocations.

Schedule 1 lists relevant EC 'product' Directives referred to in regulation 10; Schedule 2 lists the considerable amount of legislation being repealed and revoked.

Relationship with existing health and safety legislation

10   PUWER amplifies and makes more explicit the general duties on employers, the self-employed and persons in control to provide safe plant and equipment. Virtually all the requirements already exist somewhere in the law or constitute good practice. PUWER brings together these requirements and applies them across all industrial, commercial and service sectors.

11   This means that employers with well chosen and well maintained equipment should need to do little more than before. Some older equipment may need to be up-graded to meet the requirements, and there is until 1 January 1997 to do the necessary work. Much old legislation - 17 codes of Regulations, seven sections of the Factories Act 1961, one section of the Offices, Shops and Railway Premises Act 1963 and two sections of the Mines and Quarries Act 1954 - is being replaced, in full or in part, by PUWER although most will continue to apply to existing equipment until 1 January 1997 when the transitional period ends.

12   PUWER will overlap many existing requirements but where this occurs compliance with the existing requirement should normally be sufficient to comply with PUWER. For example, the requirement concerning isolation from sources of energy (regulation 19) is, so far as electricity is concerned, dealt with by the Electricity at Work Regulations 1989. Another example is that scaffolds which have been properly maintained under the Construction (Working Places) Regulations 1966 will also meet the requirements for maintenance under PUWER.

Relationship with other new health and safety legislation

13   In addition to the Provision and Use of Work Equipment Regulations, the following Regulations (which also stem from recent European Directives) are also due to come into force in 1993:

The Management of Health and Safety at Work Regulations 1992

The Personal Protective Equipment at Work Regulations 1992

The Workplace (Health, Safety and Welfare) Regulations 1992

The Manual Handling Operations Regulations 1992

The Health and Safety (Display Screen Equipment) Regulations 1992

14   These new Regulations will operate alongside the HSW Act and Regulations made under the HSW Act, for example, the Electricity at Work Regulations 1989, the Noise at Work Regulations 1989, the Control of Substances Hazardous to Health Regulations 1988.

15   Therefore, PUWER cannot be considered in isolation. In particular, they need to be looked at together with the Management of Health and Safety at Work Regulations 1992 (MHSWR).

16   Regulation 3(1) of MHSWR requires all employers and the self-employed to assess the risks to the health and safety of workers and any others who may be affected by the work carried out, for the purpose of identifying the measures needed to be taken to comply with other legislation. Carrying out this assessment will help to identify all the protective and preventative measures that have to be taken to comply with these Regulations, particularly for regulation 5 - selection of suitable work equipment, regulation 11 - safeguarding dangerous parts of machinery and also regulations 12 to 24.

17   Further guidance on the procedure for risk assessment is to be found in the Approved Code of Practice on the MHSWR which includes advice on the selection of preventative and protective measures.

18   A common sense approach needs to be adopted to risk assessment, the most important part of which is to decide whether or not the requirements of these Regulations are already being complied with and if not, what additional measures need to be taken.

19   Most employers will be capable of making the risk assessment themselves using expertise within their own organisations to identify the measures which need to be taken concerning their work equipment. In a few cases, for example where there are complex hazards or equipment, it may need to be done in conjunction with the help of external health and safety advisors, appointed under regulation 6 of MHSWR.

20   For many items of work equipment, particularly machinery, the user will know from previous experience what measures need to be taken to comply with previous legal requirements. Generally those measures will ensure compliance with these Regulations. Where this is not the case there is usually a straightforward method of identifying the measures that need to be taken, because these are described in either general or industry specific or machine specific guidance. However, the user will need to decide whether these are appropriate.

21   Where guidance does not exist, or is not appropriate, the main factors that need to be taken into account are the severity of any likely injury or ill health likely to result from any hazard present, the likelihood of that happening and the numbers exposed, to identify the measures that need to be taken to eliminate or reduce the risk to an acceptable level.

22   There are complementary training requirements in PUWER and MHSWR. Regulation 11 of MHSWR is a general requirement dealing with when health and safety training should be provided, ie on recruitment or on being exposed to new or increased risks, such as with the introduction of new technology or systems of work, or the introduction or change of work equipment. Regulation 9 of PUWER is concerned more specifically with what training should consist of, ie the precautions to be taken during the use of work equipment. MHSWR also amends the Safety Representatives and Safety Committees Regulations 1977. Safety representatives appointed under those Regulations will also have a role to play in the operation of PUWER, eg in the selection process of suitable work equipment and in its subsequent maintenance procedures.

23   There are limited areas of overlap between PUWER, the Workplace (Health, Safety and Welfare) Regulations 1992 and the Health and Safety (Display Screen Equipment) Regulations 1992 (eg on lighting) and the Personal Protective Equipment at Work Regulations 1992 (eg on maintenance). The guiding principle will be that where duties overlap, compliance with the more specific Regulation will normally be sufficient to comply with a general requirement.

Duties on manufacturers and suppliers

24   Manufacturers and suppliers of work equipment also have general legal duties under existing law and this too is being changed as the result of European Directives. These Directives, concerning products, are an essential part of the 'Single Market' which is due to be completed by 31 December 1992. In simple terms, the 'Single Market' means that manufacturers will be able to market their products without barriers to trade anywhere in the European Community providing these products meet essential health and safety requirements which have been agreed by Member States. In this context the most important 'product directive' is the Machinery Directive (89/392/EEC as amended by 91/368/EEC).

25   The Machinery Directive is concerned with health and safety through the design and construction of new machines and so corresponds most directly to the requirements of section 6 of the HSW Act. In common with other 'New Approach' Directives it sets out in general terms the essential health and safety requirements which must be met before new machinery is placed on the market. European harmonised standards will fill in the detail of these general requirements. The Directive will be implemented in the UK by Regulations made by the Department of Trade and Industry, due to take effect from 1 January 1993.

26   Equipment which satisfies these 'product' Directives will be exempt from many of the specific requirements contained in PUWER, ie regulations 11 to 24 (see guidance to regulation 10).

Duties on employees

27   The prime duty for ensuring health and safety rests with employers but employees have legal duties too, particularly under Sections 7 and 8 of the HSW Act. They include:

(a)   taking reasonable care for their own health and safety and that of others who may be affected by what they do or don't do;
(b)   co-operating with their employer on health and safety;
(c)   not interfering with or misusing anything provided for their health, safety and welfare.

These duties have been supplemented by regulation 12 of MHSWR. One of the new requirements is that employees should use correctly all work items provided by their employer in accordance with their training and the instructions they receive to enable them to use the items safely.

28   This is very relevant to employees using work equipment. It means that employees who have received the necessary and appropriate instructions and training are required to use their work equipment correctly. They should not use portable electric drilling machines in the rain (unless they have been designed and constructed for use in such conditions), move mobile tower scaffolds except from the ground, use tractors with unguarded power take-off shafts, use welding equipment in confined spaces with inadequate ventilation, or bypass safety devices (unless expressly authorised and additional precautions are taken). On machines, where particular care is needed, eg woodworking machines, they should adjust guards in line with the work to be carried out and correctly use push sticks, jigs, holders, etc.

Regulation 1

Citation and commencement

-(1) These Regulations may be cited as the Provision and Use of Work Equipment Regulations 1992.

(2) Subject to paragraph(3), these Regulations shall come into force on 1st January 1993.

(3) Regulations 11 to 24 and 27 and Schedule 2 in so far as they apply to work equipment first provided for use in the premises or undertaking before 1st January 1993 shall come into force on 1st January 1997.

Guidance

29   The Regulations come into force on 1 January 1993, subject to the exceptions in regulation 1(3). Some of the Regulations do not apply to certain categories of work equipment until 1 January 1997. The date of application will depend on whether the equipment is new, existing, second-hand, hired or leased; this is set out in the following paragraphs.

New work equipment

30   All the Regulations come into force on 1 January 1993. Items of work equipment provided for use from that date ('new equipment') will need to meet these requirements.

Existing work equipment

31   Regulations 1 to 10 come into force on 1 January 1993. Regulations 11 to 24, 27 and Schedule 2 do not come into force until 1 January 1997 for work equipment first provided for use in a particular premises or undertaking before 1 January 1993 ('existing equipment'). This means that existing equipment will be exempt from the specific requirements in regulations 11 to 24, but will continue to be subject to the existing legislation (listed in Schedule 2) during this period. The provisions of regulations 11 to 24 are generally specific 'hardware' provisions, ie they prescribe features that relate to the equipment itself. Employers with well chosen and well maintained existing equipment should need to do little more than at present. Some older equipment may need to be up-graded to meet the requirements, but there is time to do any necessary work until 1 January 1997.

Second-hand work equipment

32   When existing work equipment is sold by one company to another and brought into use by the second company from 1 January 1993 onwards, it becomes 'new equipment' in the sense of paragraph 30, even though it is second-hand. This means that the purchasing company will need to ascertain that the equipment meets the specific hardware provisions of regulations 11 to 24 before putting it into use. However, it will not have to comply with the 'essential safety requirements' of Article 100A Directives (see paragraph 99) as these are not retrospective.

Hired and leased equipment

33   Hired and leased equipment is treated in the same way as second-hand equipment. This means that existing equipment hired or leased to another company from 1 January 1993 is treated as 'new equipment' in the sense of paragraph 30. Therefore, companies hiring or leasing an existing item of work equipment from 1 January 1993 onwards will need to check that it meets the

specific hardware provisions of regulations 11 to 24 before putting it into use. However, it will not have to comply with the 'essential safety requirements' of Article 100A Directives (see paragraph 99) as these are not retrospective.

First provided for use

34   The phrase 'first provided for use' refers to the date on which work equipment is first supplied in the premises or undertaking. This is not the same as first brought into use. Provided for use does not necessarily mean that it has actually been put to use. For example, equipment delivered to one of a company's premises before 1 January 1993 would be considered to be 'existing equipment', even though it might remain in store and not be put into use until after that date. (This is also relevant in the context of regulation 10.)

Premises or undertaking

35   Section 53 of the HSW Act defines premises in very wide terms to include any place and would cover individual plants, establishments, buildings, office blocks, shops, mines, offshore installations.

36   Some premises will be the sole premises owned by that employer. Others will be part of a larger undertaking with many separate premises, for example a chain of shops or tyre stockists, a university with buildings scattered throughout a city, a company with plants throughout Great Britain, or a plant-hire company with many depots. Some employees may not have a fixed place of work, eg peripatetic workers such as foresters, contract gardeners, service engineers, but the work equipment that they use is part of the employer's undertaking.

37   Work equipment which was first provided for use before 1 January 1993 at one premises belonging to an undertaking, and moved to other premises of the same undertaking on or after 1 January 1993 will be treated as existing equipment, and will have until 1 January 1997 to conform with the specific hardware provisions of these Regulations (regulations 11 to 24).

Examples

38   Examples of equipment remaining within the same undertaking are:

(a)   an engineering company which owns an existing lathe moves it from its plant in Cheshire to another one in Northumberland;

(b)   a leased radiation gauge is transferred from a paper mill in southern England to a mill in Scotland owned by the same undertaking;

(c)   a plant-hire company moves a crane or lift-truck from a depot it owns in Leeds to one in Swansea.

In all cases, the specific hardware requirements of the Regulations would not apply until 1 January 1997, providing the equipment is used by the same undertaking.

39   But if on or after 1 January 1993 the lathe is obtained by another separate undertaking or company second-hand, the radiation gauge is leased by a different company, or the crane or lift-truck is hired to a contractor on a construction site, the equipment would have been provided for use as if it were 'new equipment', and the Regulations would so apply when the equipment was used in the second undertaking.

1

Regulation 2   Interpretation

-(1) In these Regulations, unless the context otherwise requires -

"use" in relation to work equipment means any activity involving work equipment and includes starting, stopping, programming, setting, transporting, repairing, modifying, maintaining, servicing and cleaning, and related expressions shall be construed accordingly;

"work equipment" means any machinery, appliance, apparatus or tool and any assembly of components which, in order to achieve a common end, are arranged and controlled so that they function as a whole.

(2)   Any reference in these Regulations to -

(a)   a numbered regulation or Schedule is a reference to the regulation or Schedule in these Regulations so numbered; and

(b)   a numbered paragraph is a reference to the paragraph so numbered in the regulation in which the reference appears.

Guidance

40   The definition of 'use' is wide and includes all activities involving the work equipment such as stopping or starting the equipment, repair, modification, maintenance and servicing. In addition to operations normally considered as use, cleaning and transport of the equipment are also included. In this context 'transport' means, for example, using a lift truck to carry goods around a warehouse.

41   The scope of 'work equipment' is also extremely wide. Work equipment includes single machines such as a power press, guillotine, circular saw bench, photocopier or a combine harvester, tools such as a portable drill or a hammer, and apparatus such as laboratory apparatus (bunsen burners etc). In addition to individual items of work equipment, any assembly arranged and controlled to function as a whole is included, for example a bottling plant.

42   Motor vehicles which are not privately owned fall within the scope of the Regulations. However, the more specific road traffic legislation will take precedence when these vehicles are used on public roads. When such vehicles are used off the public highway these Regulations and the HSW Act would normally take precedence.

43   By way of example, the following is a non-exhaustive list of work equipment subject to these Regulations:

WORK EQUIPMENT

dumper truck	ladder	portable drill
combine harvester	mobile access platform	scalpel
X-ray baggage detector	car ramp	soldering iron
check-out machine	trench sheets	hammer
air compressor	laboratory apparatus	meat cleaver
lawn-mower	potato grading line	butcher's knife
automatic car wash	fire engine turntable	drill bit
computer	resuscitator	socket set
crane	detonator	hand saw
power press	microbiological safety cabinet	scaffolder's podger
road tanker	photoelectric device	
tractor	lifting sling	
lift truck		
power harrow		
vehicle hoist		
overhead projector		

Guidance

2

dry cleaning unit	robot line
drilling equipment for use on an offshore installation	blast furnace
	automatic storage and retrieval equipment
pit winding gear	
reactor	solvent degreasing bath
scaffolding	LPG filling plant
cooling tower	quarry crushing plant
pressure vessel	nickel plating line
installed plant (eg for electricity generation)	linear accelerator

NOT WORK EQUIPMENT

livestock, substances (eg acids, alkalis, slurry, cement, water), structural items (walls, stairs, roof), private car.

Regulation 3

Regulation

3

Disapplication of these Regulations

These Regulations shall not apply to or in relation to the master or crew of a sea-going ship or to the employer of such persons, in respect of the normal ship-board activities of a ship's crew under the direction of the master.

Guidance

3

44   The Regulations have general application and apart from the exemption defined in this Regulation, apply wherever the HSW Act applies, ie to all industrial sectors, including offshore oil and gas installations, service occupations, hospitals, universities etc. The HSW Act applies throughout Great Britain and has effect wherever work is done by the employed or the self-employed other than domestic work in a private household. The HSW Act also applies to non-domestic premises made available as places of work.

Sea-going ships

45   Sea-going ships are subject to separate Merchant Shipping legislation administered by the Department of Transport. The Provision and Use of Work Equipment Regulations 1992 do not apply to the normal shipboard activities of a ship's crew under the direction of the master. However, the Regulations may apply to other activities aboard a ship, for example where a shore-based contractor carries out the work, provided the ship is within territorial waters. The Regulations also apply to certain activities carried out offshore - see regulation 26.

Regulation 4

Regulation

4

Application of requirements under these Regulations

-(1)   The requirements imposed by these Regulations on an employer shall apply in respect of work equipment provided for use or used by any of his employees who is at work or who is on an offshore installation within the meaning assigned to that term by section 1(4) of the Offshore Safety Act 1992[a]

(2)   The requirements imposed by these Regulations on an employer shall also apply -

(a) 1992 c.15

*(a) to a self-employed person, in respect of work equipment he uses at
work;*

*(b) to any person who has control, to any extent, of non-domestic premises
made available to persons as a place of work, in respect of work equipment
used in such premises by such persons and to the extent of his control; and*

*(c) to any person to whom the provisions of the Factories Act 1961[(b)] apply
by virtue of section 175(5) of that Act as if he were the occupier of a
factory, in respect of work equipment used in the premises deemed to be a
factory by that section.*

*(3) Any reference in paragraph (2)(b) to a person having control of any
premises or matter is a reference to the person having control of the premises or matter
in connection with the carrying on by him of a trade, business or other undertaking
(whether for profit or not).*

(b) 1961 c.34.

46   Employers have a general duty under Section 2 of the Health and Safety
at Work etc Act 1974 to provide and maintain, so far as is reasonably
practicable, machinery, equipment and other plant that is safe. They must also
ensure that, so far as is reasonably practicable, the systems of work are safe.
Persons in control of non-domestic premises also have a duty under Section 4
of the Act towards those who are not their employees but use their premises.
These Regulations build on those duties.

47   Employers (whether individuals, partnerships or companies) have a duty
to ensure that items of work equipment provided to their employees and the
self-employed working for them complies with these Regulations. The self-
employed must comply with the same duties in respect of work equipment they
use at work. Persons in control of non-domestic premises who provide items of
work equipment which is used by other people at work must also comply with
the Regulations. For example, the owner of a multi-occupied building has a
legal responsibility to ensure that a lift complies with the Regulations, and the
main contractor of a construction site would be responsible for a scaffold.

48   The Regulations cover not only the normal situation where employers
provide work equipment for their employees, but also cover the situation where
employers choose to allow their employees to provide their own work equipment.

49   There are no separate duties on employees in these Regulations. These
are covered in other legislation, in particular in Section 7 of the HSW Act and
regulation 12 of the MHSWR (see also paragraphs 27 to 28).

50   The Regulations place duties on **all** employers providing work equipment
to ensure that it is suitable, properly maintained etc. On multi-occupancy or
multi-contractor sites where more than one employer uses the same piece of
equipment, these duties can be discharged by the employers making
arrangements among themselves whereby one of them takes responsibility for
the measures necessary to discharge the duties in respect of that piece of
equipment, provided that the arrangements are adequate and that they work
effectively. Regulation 9 of the MHSWR and its supporting Approved Code of
Practice is relevant here. It requires employers and the self- employed who
share a workplace to coordinate their activities, cooperate with each other and
share information to ensure that each complies with their responsibilities under
health and safety legislation. The following paragraphs examine such situations
in detail in the construction and offshore sectors. Similar principles should
apply in other sectors.

Application to the construction industry

51   In the construction industry items of work equipment on sites are often used by a number of different contractors. Regulation 4 places a duty on each individual contractor to ensure that any work equipment used by their employees (or themselves in the case of self-employed contractors) conforms to, and is used in accordance with, these Regulations. It is recognised that it may sometimes be difficult to fully comply with this requirement. For example, a contractor who occasionally uses an item of machinery provided by another contractor may have little control over maintenance arrangements. Effective coordination between the parties involved is therefore essential.

52   The arrangements required by regulation 9 of the MHSWR would be strengthened by the proposed Construction (Design and Management) Regulations which are due to come into force on 31 December 1993.

53   These proposals would require the appointment of a single person or firm ('the principal contractor') who would be responsible for coordinating the activities of all the contractors on site and ensuring that work is carried out safely. The principal contractor would have a duty to ensure that all contractors cooperated.

54   Where work equipment is shared by a number of contractors the principal contractor would be required to coordinate its provision and use. Depending on the type of equipment, the nature of the project and the contractual arrangements, the principal contractor would have the option of either taking action themselves to achieve compliance with the Regulations on behalf of the common users or directing another contractor or group of contractors to do so. Cooperation and exchanging information is vital in such circumstances to ensure that faults or changes in conditions of use are reported to the coordinator for the equipment and that instructions or limitations on use are passed on to the common users.

55   Although the proposed Regulations are not due to come into force until 31 December 1993, the principle of a single coordinator for the provision and use of shared work equipment has advantages and it it is recommended that it be followed in the meantime. However, it should be noted that the establishment of such arrangements, either on an informal basis or following the introduction of the Construction (Design and Management) Regulations, does not relieve the individual contractors from their duties under regulation 4. If a breach of the law should occur as a result of a failure in the common arrangements, the balance of blameworthiness between the various parties involved would be judged on the facts of the case.

Application to the offshore industry

56   Similar considerations apply in respect of the offshore industry, where owners of installations may provide equipment for use by contractors. Owners and contractors will need to make effective arrangements for coordination and communication to ensure that the duties of regulation 4 are met.

57   These matters will also be considered in the context of the Offshore Installation (Safety Case) Regulations 1992 (expected to come into force during 1993), which will place a duty on owners or operators to demonstrate in their Safety Case that their management system is adequate to ensure that relevant statutory provisions in respect of the installation and connected activities will be complied with.

58   Effective arrangements for cooperation and coordination will also be needed to cover maintenance arrangements, to take account of the

responsibilities on individual employers under these Regulations, and on owners of offshore installations and offshore installation managers under the Offshore Installations (Operational Safety, Health and Welfare) Regulations 1976 (SI 1976/1019).

59   Equipment for use on offshore installations has to be certified as fit for purpose by independent certifying authorities under the Offshore Installations (Construction and Survey) Regulations 1974 (SI 1974/289). The Provision and Use of Work Equipment Regulations do not relieve individual employers of their duties under these Regulations.

Regulation 5

Suitability of work equipment

-(1) Every employer shall ensure that work equipment is so constructed or adapted as to be suitable for the purpose for which it is used or provided.

(2)   In selecting work equipment, every employer shall have regard to the working conditions and to the risks to the health and safety of persons which exist in the premises or undertaking in which that work equipment is to be used and any additional risk posed by the use of that work equipment.

(3)   Every employer shall ensure that work equipment is used only for operations for which, and under conditions for which, it is suitable.

(4)   In this regulation "suitable" means suitable in any respect which it is reasonably foreseeable will affect the health or safety of any person.

60   This Regulation lies at the heart of this set of Regulations. It addresses the safety of work equipment from three aspects:

(a)   its initial integrity;
(b)   the place where it will be used; and
(c)   the purpose for which it will be used.

61   The selection of suitable work equipment for particular tasks and processes makes it possible to reduce or eliminate many risks to the health and safety of people at the workplace. This applies both to the normal use of the equipment as well as to other operations such as maintenance.

62   The risk assessment carried out under regulation 3(1) of the Management of Health and Safety at Work Regulations 1992 will help employers to select work equipment and assess its suitability for particular tasks.

Regulation 5(1)

63   Equipment must be suitable, by design, construction or adaptation, for the actual work it is provided to do. This should mean in practice that when employers provide equipment they should ensure that it has been produced for the work to be undertaken and that it is used in accordance with the manufacturer's specifications and instructions. If employers choose to adapt equipment then they must ensure that it is still suitable for its intended purpose.

64   This requirement provides the focal point for the other Regulations - for example compliance with regulation 10 should ensure the initial integrity of equipment in many cases, and compliance as appropriate with the specific

11

requirements of regulations 11 to 24 should help the employer to meet the duties under this Regulation. For example, regulation 11(3)(h) deals with aspects of the integrity of guards and protection devices, and regulation 22 with the design and putting into use of work equipment that can be safely maintained.

Regulation 5(2)

65   This requires employers to assess the location in which the work equipment is to be used and to take account of any risks that may arise from the particular circumstances - for example, is the equipment to be used in a wet environment, or in a flammable atmosphere? Such factors can invalidate the use of equipment in a particular location which would be perfectly adequate to do the work in other locations. This would be the case for electrically powered equipment in wet or flammable atmospheres. In such circumstances the employer should consider the selection of pneumatically or hydraulically powered equipment or electrical equipment designed for use under such conditions.

66   Employers should also take into account the fact that work equipment itself can sometimes cause risks to health and safety in particular locations which would otherwise be safe, for example, a petrol generator discharging exhaust fumes into an enclosed space.

Regulation 5(3)

67   This requirement concerns each particular process for which the work equipment is to be used and the conditions under which it will be used. The employer must ensure that the equipment is suitable for the process and conditions of use.

68   A crane already in use would not be suitable for any particular operation where the load to be lifted exceeded its rated load. Similarly, a circular saw is generally not suitable for cutting a rebate whereas a spindle moulding machine would be because it can be guarded to a high standard; knives with unprotected blades are often used for cutting operations where scissors or other cutting tools could be used with risk of less serious injury.

Regulation 6

Maintenance

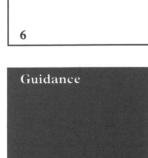

-(1) Every employer shall ensure that work equipment is maintained in an efficient state, in efficient working order and in good repair.

(2) Every employer shall ensure that where any machinery has a maintenance log, the log is kept up to date.

69   This Regulation, which builds on the more general duty in the HSW Act, deals with the obligation to maintain equipment, not the need for such maintenance to be carried out safely. The latter is however a requirement of Section 2 of the HSW Act. The design of the equipment so that maintenance can be carried out without risk to health or safety is the subject of regulation 22 for existing work equipment and regulation 10 for new equipment.

70   In regulation 6, 'efficient' relates to how the condition of the equipment might affect health and safety; it is not concerned with productivity. Some parts of equipment such as guards, ventilation equipment, emergency

shutdown systems and pressure relief devices clearly have to be maintained to do their job at all times. The necessity to maintain other parts may not be as obvious, but as an example failure to lubricate bearings or replace clogged filters might lead to danger because of seized parts or overheating.

71   It is important that equipment is maintained so that its performance does not deteriorate to the extent that it puts people at risk. The extent and complexity of maintenance will vary enormously, from simple checks on hand-held tools (for example to identify loose heads on hammers or splayed mushroom heads on chisels) to a substantial integrated programme for a complex process plant.

72   Equipment may need to be checked frequently to ensure that safety-related features are functioning correctly. A fault which affects production is normally apparent within a short time, however a fault in a safety critical system could remain undetected unless maintenance procedures provide adequate inspection or testing. The frequency at which equipment needs to be checked is dependent on the equipment itself and the risk involved; it could be each day, every three months, or even longer.

73   Any maintenance work should only be done by those who have received adequate information, instructions and training relating to that work; these should cover the reasons for the maintenance activities as well as the procedures and techniques which are applied; see also regulations 8 and 9.

74   In addition to any requirement to carry out maintenance under this regulation, other legislation may set out minimum requirements for maintenance or for inspection or test. Examples are specific requirements for hoists, lifts, scaffolds and control measures such as ventilation plant. However, although minimum requirements may have been set, there is still a need for the equipment to be effectively maintained at all times.

Routine maintenance

75   This includes periodic lubrication, inspection and testing, based on the recommendations of the equipment manufacturer; it should also take account of any specific legal requirements as indicated in paragraph 74. However, while in most cases it would be expected that the combination of the manufacturer's instructions and legal requirements would allow adequate maintenance, in particularly arduous conditions, for example, further measures may be required.

76   Components which are found to have failed or are likely to fail before the next periodic check should be repaired or replaced. In some cases, faults may have occurred which are not immediately apparent.

Planned preventive maintenance

77   When inadequate maintenance could cause the equipment, guards or other protection devices to fail in a dangerous way, a formal system of planned preventive maintenance may be necessary.

78   Although all maintenance is preventive in some respect, the primary aim of planned preventive maintenance is to prevent failures occurring while the equipment is in use.

79   This is achieved through a system of written instructions which are used to initiate inspection, testing and, perhaps more importantly, the periodic replacement or refurbishing of components or equipment before they reach the

13

end of their useful life. The instructions could be based as appropriate on the manufacturer's recommendations or experience from previous service and condition monitoring.

Maintenance log

80 There is no requirement for a maintenance log. However, it is recommended that a record of maintenance is kept. A maintenance log should provide information for future planning and inform maintenance personnel and others of previous action taken. This may be of value in complying with the requirements of regulation 8(3).

81 If there is a log, it should be kept up-to-date. Other legislation for particular types of equipment may require records of maintenance to be provided in a specified way, especially when this includes testing.

Regulation 7

Specific risks

Regulation

7

-*(1) Where the use of work equipment is likely to involve a specific risk to health or safety, every employer shall ensure that -*

(a) *the use of that work equipment is restricted to those persons given the task of using it; and*

(b) *repairs, modifications, maintenance or servicing of that work equipment is restricted to those persons who have been specifically designated to perform operations of that description (whether or not also authorised to perform other operations).*

(2) The employer shall ensure that the persons designated for the purposes of sub-paragraph (b) of paragraph (1) have received adequate training related to any operations in respect of which they have been so designated.

82 This Regulation implements a requirement of the Directive. HSE takes the view that no additional measures, other than those required by existing legislation, need to be taken by industry to comply with this Regulation. Those responsible for enforcement (HSE inspectors and local authority inspectors) are aware of this.

Regulation 8

Information and instructions

Regulation

8

-*(1) Every employer shall ensure that all persons who use work equipment have available to them adequate health and safety information and, where appropriate, written instructions pertaining to the use of the work equipment.*

(2) Every employer shall ensure that any of his employees who supervises or manages the use of work equipment has available to him adequate health and safety information and, where appropriate, written instructions pertaining to the use of the work equipment.

(3) Without prejudice to the generality of paragraphs (1) or (2), the information and instructions required by either of those paragraphs shall include

information and, where appropriate, written instructions on-

(a)   the conditions in which and the methods by which the work equipment may be used;

(b)   foreseeable abnormal situations and the action to be taken if such a situation were to occur; and

(c)   any conclusions to be drawn from experience in using the work equipment.

(4)   Information and instructions required by this regulation shall be readily comprehensible to those concerned.

83   This Regulation builds on the general duty in the HSW Act to provide employees with such information and instruction as is necessary to ensure, so far as is reasonably practicable, their health and safety. In addition, it complements the general requirement in the Management of Health and Safety at Work Regulations 1992 to provide information to employees relating to their health and safety. It places a duty on employers to make available all relevant health and safety information and written instructions on the use of work equipment to their workforce. This means that the workforce should have easy access to such information and instructions and be able to understand them.

84   Information can be in writing or verbal where this is considered to be sufficient. It is the employer's responsibility to decide, given the individual circumstances, which is appropriate. Where there are more complicated or unusual situations the information should be in writing. The employer will need to take into account such matters as the degree of skill of the employees involved, their experience and training, the degree of supervision and the complexity and length of the particular job.

85   Written instructions refer primarily to the information provided by manufacturers or suppliers such as instruction sheets or manuals, instruction placards, warning labels and training manuals. There are duties on manufacturers and suppliers to provide sufficient information, including drawings, to make possible the correct installation, safe operation and maintenance of the work equipment. Employers should ask or check that they are provided. The Regulation requires employers to ensure that such written instructions are available to those directly using the work equipment; they should not be gathering dust in the purchasing department. Maintenance instructions should be made available/passed on to those involved in the maintenance of work equipment.

86   The information and written instructions should also be available to supervisors and managers. The amount of very detailed health and safety information they will need to have immediately available for day-to-day running of production lines or research laboratories will vary but it is important that they know what information is available and where it can be found.

87   The information and written instructions should cover all the health and safety aspects of use that will arise and any limitations on these uses together with any foreseeable difficulties that could arise and the methods to deal with them. Any conclusions drawn from experience in the use of the equipment should be acted upon and either recorded or steps taken to ensure that all appropriate members of the workforce are aware of them.

88   To be readily comprehensible all information and written instructions should be presented clearly in English, and/or other languages where necessary, and be in a logical sequence with good illustrations when appropriate. Standard

symbols should be used. Account should be taken of the workforce's level of training, knowledge and experience. Special consideration should be given to any employees with language difficulties or with disabilities which may impede their receipt of information. For employees with little or no understanding of English or with reading difficulties, employers may need to make special arrangements.

Regulation 9 Training

-*(1) Every employer shall ensure that all persons who use work equipment have received adequate training for purposes of health and safety, including training in the methods which may be adopted when using the work equipment, any risks which such use may entail and precautions to be taken.*

(2) Every employer shall ensure that any of his employees who supervises or manages the use of work equipment has received adequate training for purposes of health and safety, including training in the methods which may be adopted when using the work equipment, any risks which such use may entail and precautions to be taken.

89   An employer's obligation to train extends not only to those who use work equipment but also to those supervising or managing them. The training should be adequate for the circumstances.

90   It is impossible to lay down detailed requirements as to what constitutes 'adequate training' in all circumstances. In considering the extent of training which will be necessary in a particular case, the shortfall between the employee's existing competence and that necessary to use, supervise or manage the use of the work equipment with due regard to health and safety, will need to be evaluated and made up. Account should be taken of the circumstances in which the employee is to work (eg alone, under close supervision of a competent person, in a supervisory or management capacity.)

91   The development of specific statements of what the employee needs to do and to what level (ie statements of competence) will assist the employer to evaluate the extent of any shortfall in the employee's competence.

92   Statements of competence may be embodied in qualifications accredited by the National Council for Vocational Qualifications (NCVQ) and the Scottish Vocational Education Council (SCOTVEC).

Training requirements in other legislation

93   Training and instruction is a central requirement of both the HSW Act and of many specific Regulations. Regulation 11 of the Management of Health and Safety at Work Regulations 1992 requires employers to provide their employees with general health and safety training. This should be supplemented as necessary with more specific training on the use of work equipment. The detailed training requirements in, for example, the Woodworking Machines Regulations 1974 and the Abrasive Wheels Regulations 1970 are not replaced by these Regulations and will continue to apply.

Additional requirements for young people

94   Training, coupled with proper supervision, is particularly important for all young people because of their relative immaturity and unfamiliarity with the working environment. Induction training is of particular importance. In addition, there are specific training requirements in current legislation that will continue to apply to young people using certain machines, including Section 21 of the Factories Act 1961, Section 19 of the Offices, Shops and Railway Premises Act 1963, and regulation 13 of the Woodworking Machines Regulations 1974.

Regulation 10

Conformity with Community requirements

-(1)   Every employer shall ensure that any item of work equipment provided for use in the premises or undertaking of the employer complies with any enactment (whether in an Act or instrument) which implements in Great Britain any of the relevant Community Directives listed in Schedule 1 which is applicable to that item of work equipment.

(2)   Where it is shown that an item of work equipment complies with an enactment (whether in an Act or instrument) to which it is subject by virtue of paragraph (1), the requirements of regulations 11 to 24 shall apply in respect of that item of work equipment only to the extent that the relevant Community directive implemented by that enactment is not applicable to that item of work equipment.

(3)   This regulation applies to items of work equipment provided for use in the premises or undertaking of the employer for the first time after 31st December 1992.

95   This Regulation aims to ensure that when work equipment is first provided for use in the workplace after 31 December 1992 it meets certain health and safety requirements. It places a duty on employers that complements those on manufacturers and suppliers in other legislation regarding the initial integrity of equipment.

96   There are legal requirements covering all those involved in the chain of supply of work equipment which are designed to ensure that new work equipment is safe. For example, Section 6 of the HSW Act, which will remain in force, places general duties on designers, manufacturers, importers and suppliers to ensure this so far as is reasonably practicable.

97   Existing national legislation on the manufacture and supply of new work equipment is increasingly being supplemented by new and more detailed Regulations implementing EC Directives made under Article 100A of the Treaty of Rome. These new Regulations place duties on the manufacturer and supplier of new work equipment. (Further background to the Article 100A Directives is set out in paragraphs 102 to 106.)

Regulation 10(1)

98   Regulation 10(1) places a new duty on employers as users of work equipment. When first providing work equipment for use in the workplace they should ensure that it has been made to the requirements of the legislation implementing any product Directive which is relevant to the equipment. (For interpretation of 'first provided for use' see the guidance on regulation 1.) In practice this may mean that whereas previously employers would have specified

to the supplier that work equipment should comply with current health and safety legislation, they would in future also specify that it should comply with the legislation implementing any relevant EC Directive. Where appropriate the employer can check to see that the equipment bears a CE mark and ask for a copy of the EC Declaration of Conformity.

99   The position is complicated because at present not all work equipment is covered by a product Directive. Nor are product Directives retrospective. If an employer provides second-hand equipment for the first time in the workplace it does not need to be modified to meet the 'essential safety requirements' of the relevant product Directive, but it must comply immediately with regulations 11 to 24 of PUWER. (Second-hand equipment imported from outside the European Community has to comply immediately with the 'essential safety requirements' of the relevant product Directive.)

100   One of the most significant relevant Directives is the Machinery Directive, for which the Department of Trade and Industry has lead responsibility. This applies to machinery that is first placed on the market from 1/1/93 (but not to second-hand machinery unless it is being imported from outside the European Community). This will be implemented in this country by the proposed Machinery (Safety) Regulations. There is a transitional period from 1 January 1993 to 1 January 1995, where the manufacturer has the choice of either placing machinery on the market in accordance with the 'essential safety requirements' of those Directives and CE marked **or** of continuing to comply with the national legislation in force on 31 December 1992.

Regulation 10(2)

101   Regulation 10(2) means that if the work equipment complies with the implementing legislation of the relevant product Directive, then any corresponding requirements in regulations 11 to 24 will not apply (see Appendix 1).

Article 100A Directives

102   The aim of this group of Directives is to achieve the free movement of goods in the Community Single Market by eliminating differing national controls and harmonising essential technical requirements. Many of these Directives have been made within a common structure which was set out in a resolution of the Council of Ministers in 1985. These Directives are often called 'New Approach' Directives. Examples important to safety at work include the Machinery Directive, the Personal Protective Equipment Directive and the Simple Pressure Vessels Directive. Others are still in negotiation (eg a 2nd Amendment to the Machinery Directive and a Directive on Pressure Equipment).

103   These New Approach Directives set out 'essential safety requirements' which must be met before products may be sold in the Community. Products which comply with the Directives must be given free circulation within the Community. These Directives also apply to equipment made and put into service in-house. Suppliers must ensure that their products when placed on the market comply with the legal requirements implementing the Directives applicable to their product. It is a common feature of these Directives that compliance is claimed by the manufacturer affixing a mark - the 'CE Mark' - to the equipment. (At present the CE Mark has slightly differing meanings depending on the Directive concerned; negotiations are underway to ensure that the mark has the same meaning across the range of 'New Approach' Directives.)

104   One way of demonstrating compliance with the 'essential safety requirements' applicable to a product will be by designing and manufacturing

to harmonised standards. These are standards made by the European Standardisation Bodies - CEN and CENELEC - under a mandate from the Commission of the European Communities to which a reference has been published in the Official Journal of the European Communities. When developed these harmonised standards will be transposed in the UK by the British Standards Institution and will bear a common number (ie EN XXXX will be BS EN XXXX here). In practice it is expected that most manufacturers will design and construct products according to these standards - although their use is voluntary.

105 Once these Directives are fully in force only products which conform and bear the 'CE Mark' may be placed on the market in the UK.

106 A list of relevant Directives is in Schedule 1 of the Regulations and this includes a number of EC product Directives which pre-date the 'New Approach' Directives but which also specify the requirements which must be met before the products are placed on the market.

Regulation 11

Dangerous parts of machinery

-*(1) Every employer shall ensure that measures are taken in accordance with paragraph (2) which are effective -*

    (a)   to prevent access to any dangerous part of machinery or to any rotating stock-bar; or

    (b)   to stop the movement of any dangerous part of machinery or rotating stock-bar before any part of a person enters a danger zone.

    (2)   The measures required by paragraph (1) shall consist of-

    (a)   the provision of fixed guards enclosing every dangerous part or rotating stock-bar where and to the extent that it is practicable to do so, but where or to the extent that it is not, then

    (b)   the provision of other guards or protection devices where and to the extent that it is practicable to do so, but where or to the extent that it is not, then

    (c)   the provision of jigs, holders, push-sticks or similar protection appliances used in conjunction with the machinery where and to the extent that it is practicable to do so, but where or to the extent that it is not, then

    (d)   the provision of information, instruction, training and supervision.

    (3)   All guards and protection devices provided under sub-paragraphs (a) or (b) of paragraph (2) shall -

    (a)   be suitable for the purpose for which they are provided;

    (b)   be of good construction, sound material and adequate strength;

    (c)   be maintained in an efficient state, in efficient working order and in good repair;

(d)   not give rise to any increased risk to health or safety;

(e)   not be easily bypassed or disabled;

(f)   be situated at sufficient distance from the danger zone;

(g)   not unduly restrict the view of the operating cycle of the machinery, where such a view is necessary;

(h)   be so constructed or adapted that they allow operations necessary to fit or replace parts and for maintenance work, restricting access so that it is allowed only to the area where the work is to be carried out and, if possible, without having to dismantle the guard or protection device.

(4)   All protection appliances provided under sub-paragraph (c) of paragraph (2) shall comply with sub-paragraphs (a) to (d) and (g) of paragraph (3).

(5)   In this regulation -

"danger zone" means any zone in or around machinery in which a person is exposed to a risk to health or safety from contact with a dangerous part of machinery or a rotating stock-bar;

"stock-bar" means any part of a stock-bar which projects beyond the head-stock of a lathe.

107   This Regulation covers risks arising from most mechanical hazards, and replaces most of the existing legal requirements for the guarding of machinery. Unlike the old laws, the Regulation applies across all industrial and service sectors. For information on the time and circumstances when these Regulations take the place of the old laws, see the guidance to regulation 1 and 27.

108   Regulation 11(1) sets out the principal duty, to take effective measures to prevent contact with dangerous parts of machinery. The measures must either prevent access to the dangerous part, or stop the movement of the dangerous part before any part of a person can reach it. Regulation 11(2) lays down a hierarchy of preventive measures. Regulation 11(3) lists essential features of guards and protection devices. Regulation 11(4) indicates which of these features should also apply to protection appliances. Regulation 11(5) defines two terms used in this Regulation.

Regulation 11(1) - Principal duty

109   The term 'dangerous part of machinery' is well established in health and safety law. The safeguarding measures which were effective to comply with earlier law will continue to be appropriate under this Regulation, which maintains the emphasis of that law. The serious risks associated with dangerous parts of machinery have long been recognised. The technical aspects of assessing and removing these risks is a large and important subject, and full coverage is beyond the scope of this publication. Many HSC, HSE and industry-specific or machine-specific publications exist which illustrate the measures that can be taken to protect against risks associated with dangerous parts. Current national and international standards may also be used for guidance (see the reference section at the back of the publication). European harmonised standards will carry forward present standards and should be used as appropriate. Appendix 3 gives more detailed information about the available methods of safeguarding and the features they need to have in order to conform with regulation 11.

110   A risk assessment carried out under regulation 3 of the MHSWR should identify hazards presented by machinery. The types of hazard presented by machinery are described in detail in some standards (BS 5304, BS EN 292-1) and in other publications dealing with machinery safety. If the hazard could present a reasonably foreseeable risk to a person, the part of the machinery generating that hazard is a 'dangerous part'. The hazard generally results in a risk when the part of the machine is in motion. The risk assessment should evaluate the nature of the injury, its severity and likelihood of occurrence. The risk to be overcome is contact of part of the body or clothing with the dangerous part of the machine.

111   As well as parts of a machine, the Regulation also applies to contact with a rotating stock-bar which projects beyond the headstock of a lathe. This continues the protection afforded by sub-section 14(5) of the Factories Act 1961 and extends it to premises not subject to that Act.

112   Protection against other hazards associated with machinery, such as ejected particles and heat, is dealt with in other Regulations (eg 12 and 13). However, the measures used to conform with this Regulation may also be partly or fully effective in protecting against those other hazards.

Regulation 11(2) - Hierarchy of measures

113   The measures that may be taken are put into a hierarchy of four levels. The four levels are:

(a)   fixed enclosing guards;

(b)   other guards or protection devices;

(c)   protection appliances (jigs, holders, push sticks etc); and

(d)   the provision of information, instruction, training and supervision.

An explanation of the guarding and protection terms used is given in Appendix 3.

114   The hazard or hazards from machinery will be identified as part of the risk assessment. The assessment will then go on to identify measures that can be taken to overcome the risks that the hazard(s) present. In selecting measures, it is necessary to consider each level of the hierarchy in turn from the top, and use measures from that level as far as it is practicable to do so, provided they contribute to the reduction of risk. This will often result in a combination of measures being selected. The selection process continues down the hierarchy until the combined measures are effective in overcoming the risks and meeting the requirements of regulation 11(1).

115   The selection of the appropriate combination will need to take account of the requirements of the work, the evaluation of the risks, and the technical features of possible safeguarding. Further guidance is given in Appendix 3.

116   Most machines will present more than one mechanical hazard, and the risks associated with all of these need to be dealt with. Therefore at belt conveyors there is a risk of entanglement with the rotating shafts and of being trapped by the intake between drum and moving belt and appropriate safety measures should be adopted.

117   Any risk assessment carried out under regulation 3 of the MHSWR should not just deal with the machine in its normal operating mode, but must

also cover activities such as setting, maintenance, cleaning or repair. The assessment may indicate that these activities require a different combination of measures from those appropriate to the machine doing its normal work. In particular, parts of machinery that are not dangerous in normal use because they are not then accessible may become accessible and therefore dangerous while this type of work is being done.

118 Certain setting or adjustment operations which may have to be done with the machine running may require a greater reliance on provision of information, instruction, training and supervision than is the case for normal use. A permit-to-work system may be needed to prevent those doing the work being put at risk by others. See also the guidance to regulation 22.

119 To be effective, measures provided in accordance with regulation 11(2)(b) to (d) may need to be used in particular ways (defined by training, information and instruction), and not abused. Regulation 12(1) of the MHSWR requires employees to use such measures appropriately.

Regulation 11(3) - Features of guards and protection devices and Regulation 11(4) - Features of protection appliances

120 Regulation 11(3) sets out various requirements for guards and protection devices. These are largely common sense, and in large part are detailed in relevant national and international standards. Ways of achieving satisfactory guarding and other protection are discussed in more detail in the standards and in other guidance - see the reference section. These requirements are explained in detail in Appendix 3. Regulation 11(4) similarly sets out requirements for protection appliances.

11

Regulation 12

Protection against specified hazards

-(1) Every employer shall take measures to ensure that the exposure of a person using work equipment to any risk to his health or safety from any hazard specified in paragraph (3) is either prevented, or, where that is not reasonably practicable, adequately controlled.

(2) The measures required by paragraph (1) shall -

(a) be measures other than the provision of personal protective equipment or of information, instruction, training and supervision, so far as is reasonably practicable; and

(b) include, where appropriate, measures to minimise the effects of the hazard as well as to reduce the likelihood of the hazard occurring.

(3) The hazards referred to in paragraph (1) are-

(a) any article or substance falling or being ejected from work equipment;

(b) rupture or disintegration of parts of work equipment;

(c) work equipment catching fire or overheating;

(d) the unintended or premature discharge of any article or of any gas, dust,

12

liquid, vapour or other substance which, in each case, is produced, used or stored in the work equipment;

(e)   the unintended or premature explosion of the work equipment or any article or substance produced, used or stored in it.

(4)   For the purposes of this regulation "adequate" means adequate having regard only to the nature of the hazard and the nature and degree of exposure to the risk, and "adequately" shall be construed accordingly.

(5)   This regulation shall not apply where any of the following Regulations apply in respect of any risk to a person's health or safety for which such Regulations require measures to be taken to prevent or control such risk, namely -

(a)   the Control of Lead at Work Regulations 1980(a);

(b)   the Ionising Radiations Regulations 1985(b);

(c)   the Control of Asbestos at Work Regulations 1987(c);

(d)   the Control of Substances Hazardous to Health Regulations 1988(d);

(e)   the Noise at Work Regulations 1989(e);

(f)   the Construction (Head Protection) Regulations 1989(f).

(a) S.I. 1980/1248.
(b) S.I. 1985/1333.
(c) S.I. 1987/2115; amended by S.I. 1988/712.
(d) S.I. 1988/1657; amended by S.I. 1990/2026 and
      S.I. 1991/2431.
(e) S.I. 1989/1790.
(f) S.I. 1989/2209.

12

121   This Regulation covers risks arising from certain listed hazards during the use of equipment. Examples of the hazards that the Regulation addresses are:

(a)   material falling from equipment, for example a loose board falling from scaffolding, a straw bale falling from a tractor foreloader, or molten metal spilling from a ladle;

(b)   material held in the equipment being unexpectedly thrown out, for example swarf ejected from a machine tool;

(c)   parts of the equipment breaking off and being thrown out, for example an abrasive wheel bursting;

(d)   part of the equipment coming apart, for example collapse of scaffolding or falsework;

(e)   overheating or fire due for example to friction (bearings running hot, conveyor belt on jammed roller), electric motor burning out, ignition by welding torch, thermostat failing, cooling system failure;

(f)   explosion of the equipment due to pressure build-up, perhaps due to the failure of a pressure-relief device or the unexpected blockage or sealing off of pipework;

12

(g) explosion of substance in the equipment, due for example to exothermic chemical reaction or unplanned ignition of a flammable gas or vapour or finely divided organic material (eg flour, coal dust), or welding work on a container with flammable residues.

122 A risk assessment carried out under regulation 3 of the Management of Health and Safety at Work Regulations 1992 should identify these hazards, and assess the risks associated with them. The assessment will need to consider the likelihood of such events occurring and the consequent danger if they do occur, in order to identify measures to be taken to comply with this Regulation.

123 Regulation 12(1) sets the primary aim, which is to prevent any of the events in regulation 12(3) arising, if that event exposes a person to risk. Where possible, the equipment should be designed so that events presenting a risk cannot occur. If this is not reasonably practicable, steps should be taken to reduce the risk. Examples of measures that may be taken are the monitoring of solvent concentrations at evaporating ovens to detect the build-up of explosive atmospheres, or the use of inert gas systems to control and suppress dust explosions.

124 Regulation 12(1) permits the discharge or ejection of material as an intentional or unavoidable part of the process (eg grit-blasting of castings, sawdust from woodworking), but any risks to people must be controlled. The Regulation also allows the use of equipment designed to make use of explosive forces in a controlled manner (eg an internal combustion engine or a rail detonator signal).

125 Equipment may have been designed before manufacture to eliminate or reduce the likelihood of the type of event listed in regulation 12(3). But equipment suppliers cannot control the materials used in equipment, or the environment in which it is used, and it is up to employers to ensure that the equipment is suitable for their application, as required by regulation 5(2). Therefore a factor such as high temperature, vibration or a flammable atmosphere may generate a hazard, and exposure to risks from this must be controlled.

126 Regulation 12(2)(b) requires that in addition to reducing the likelihood of the event occurring, measures must be taken to mitigate the effect of any event which does occur. An example is the use of pressure relief panels. If failure would lead to risk of injury, containment measures are needed as a back-up. An example might be a blast wall; or where there is a risk from a pressure relief panel or vent bursting, ensuring that any gases or liquids discharged are directed to a safe place, contained, or made safe as appropriate.

127 Regulation 12(2)(a) requires that risk controlling measures should be provided as part of the equipment, so far as is reasonably practicable. Personal protective equipment may be appropriate where a risk remains that cannot otherwise be eliminated.

128 Training, supervision and provision of information will often have an important role to play. First, they can help to ensure that equipment is operated in the correct way to prevent dangers occurring. Secondly, they can help to ensure that the appropriate safeguards are taken to prevent personal injury in the event of a hazard materialising.

129 Regulation 12(1) of the MHSWR requires employees to use equipment in accordance with any appropriate training and instructions they receive from employers.

130   Guidance on accepted measures to control the risks covered by this Regulation is available in publications prepared by HSC, HSE and other bodies (see the reference section at the back of this publication).

Abrasive wheels

131   One particular example of the application of these principles is the use of abrasive wheels. These Regulations replace many of the provisions of the Abrasive Wheels Regulations 1970. To minimise the risk of bursting, wheels should always be run within the specified maximum rotation speed: if they are large enough this will be marked on the wheel (in accordance with regulation 23); smaller wheels should have a notice fixed in the workroom giving the individual or class maximum permissible rotation speed. The power-driven spindle should be governed so that its rotation speed does not exceed this. Furthermore, guarding must be provided to contain fragments of the wheel that might fly off if it did burst, so as to prevent them injuring anyone in the workplace. The guarding has an additional role in helping to meet the requirements of regulation 11; it should be designed, constructed and maintained to fulfil both functions. Providing information and training of workers in the correct handling and mounting of abrasive wheels (including pre-mounting and storing procedures) is also necessary to reduce the risk of bursting.

Relationship with other legislation

132   As well as presenting risks to mechanical safety, some possible emissions or discharges may present a health hazard. Other Regulations deal with this aspect in many workplaces; they are listed in regulation 12(5). Regulation 12 does not apply where and to the extent that those other Regulations do. This means the Control of Substances Hazardous to Health Regulations (COSHH) 1988 would apply to leakage of a toxic substance, whereas regulation 12 would apply to leakage of steam or cooling water from the same equipment. Similarly, COSHH would apply to the discharge of coolant mist from a machine tool, but regulation 12 would apply in the case of ejected swarf.

133   There is other legislation which is relevant to some of the hazards dealt with in this Regulation. For general guidance on how such legislation relates to these Regulations, see paragraphs 10 to 12. Some of the most relevant legislation is listed in the following paragraphs.

134   For fire or explosion hazards, Section 31 of the Factories Act 1961 and the Highly Flammable Liquids and Liquefied Petroleum Gases Regulations 1972 apply, although only in premises subject to the Factories Act 1961. Risks from electricity include fire, arcing or igniting an explosion: these risks are covered by the Electricity at Work Regulations 1989.

135   The use of vessels and systems under pressure is subject to the Pressure Systems and Transportable Gas Containers Regulations 1989.

Regulation 13

High or very low temperature

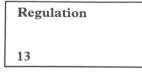

Regulation

13

Every employer shall ensure that work equipment, parts of work equipment and any article or substance produced, used or stored in work equipment which, in each case, is at a high or very low temperature shall have protection where appropriate so as to prevent injury to any person by burn, scald or sear.

136 Regulation 13 deals with the risk of injury from contact with hot or very cold work equipment, parts of work equipment or articles/substances in the work equipment. It does not cover any related risk such as radiant heat or glare.

137 Accessible surfaces of equipment or machinery, when hot or very cold, represent sources of risk of burn or other injury such as frostbite. Examples of relevant equipment might include a flat-iron, liquid nitrogen tank, gas cooker, blast furnace, snow making machine, cold store, steam pipe, etc.

138 Touching such surfaces may take place intentionally, eg to operate a handle of the equipment, or unintentionally, when someone is near the equipment. Certain work equipment is necessarily hot as part of the process and employees may have to work close to the equipment eg, foundry equipment, drop forging, hot pressing.

139 The risk from contact with hot surfaces should be reduced by engineering methods, ie reduction of surface temperature, insulation, shielding, barricading and guarding. The risk from hot process materials - contact, splashing, spilling, etc - should likewise be reduced by limiting maximum temperature, limiting liquor level, indirect steam heating methods, provision of doors, lids or covers, temperature interlocking of doors or lids and deflection systems for hot liquor (catch pan, spillway etc).

140 In many cases surfaces of equipment or devices have to be hot and accessible to operate, eg cooker hot plates, soldering iron bit, heated rolls. In such cases no engineering protective measures can be taken. In cases in which engineering protective measures can be applied, eg by reducing surface temperatures, these should be adopted in preference to personal protective measures. The choice of protective measures will need to be decided in each particular case and according to the particular circumstances.

141 While engineering measures should always be applied where appropriate, alternative or complementary forms of protection may also be necessary, eg the use of personal protective equipment (see the Personal Protective Equipment at Work Regulations 1992) and/or organisational measures such as warning signs (warning signals, visual and noise alarm signals) instructions, training, supervision, technical documentation, operating instructions, instructions for use.

Regulations 14 to 18: Controls and control systems

142 Regulations 14 to 18 require the provision of controls and certain arrangements 'where appropriate'. This qualification relates both to the features and functioning of the work equipment itself and to whether there is a risk associated with its use.

143 Start, stop and emergency stop controls are not generally appropriate where work equipment has no moving parts. Similarly they are not appropriate where the risk of injury is negligible, for example battery-powered clocks or solar-powered calculators.

144 Some types of work equipment are powered by human effort and although their use involves risk of injury, their physical characteristics and the fact that they are under close human control makes the provision of controls inappropriate; examples include the following when they use only human power: guillotines, hand-drills and lawn-mowers.

145 Other types of human-powered work equipment may not need start controls, but it may be appropriate to provide other types of control,

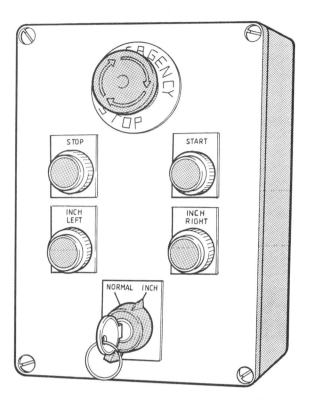

Figure 1 Control station

particularly stop controls, where the work equipment does not necessarily come to a halt when the human effort stops, for example luggage trolleys.

146   It is usually appropriate to provide all of the controls required by regulations 14 to 18 where work equipment is powered by means other than human effort (see Figure 1). The decision should be based on the risk assessment carried out as required by regulation 3 of the MHSWR (see paragraph 16 for further details).

147   The Regulations on controls and control systems do not only apply to equipment with moving parts (machinery); they may also apply to other equipment which might generate a risk, such as ovens, X-ray generators, and lasers.

148   A control is the manual actuator that the operator touches, eg a button, foot-pedal, knob, or lever. It may operate directly, but is more often a part of a control device such as a brake, clutch, switch, or relay. The control and control device are parts of the control system which may be considered as all the components which act together to monitor and control the functions of the work equipment. Control systems may operate using mechanical linkages, electricity, pneumatics, hydraulics etc, or combinations of these.

149   In practice, most individual items of equipment are likely to be provided with appropriate controls when supplied. But for complex items of equipment, or installations or assemblies comprising several different items of equipment, it may be necessary to carry out a more detailed assessment of the risks and make special provisions to ensure that controls are provided that comply fully with these Regulations.

Regulation 14 Controls for starting or making a significant change in operating conditions

-(1) Every employer shall ensure that, where appropriate, work equipment is provided with one or more controls for the purposes of -

(a) starting the work equipment (including re-starting after a stoppage for any reason); or

(b) controlling any change in the speed, pressure or other operating conditions of the work equipment where such conditions after the change result in risk to health and safety which is greater than or of a different nature from such risks before the change.

(2) Subject to paragraph (3), every employer shall ensure that where a control is required by paragraph (1), it shall not be possible to perform any operation mentioned in sub-paragraph (a) or (b) of that paragraph except by a deliberate action on such control.

(3) Paragraph (1) shall not apply to re-starting or changing operating conditions as a result of the normal operating cycle of an automatic device.

150 One or more controls must be provided, where appropriate, to start work equipment. Starting should only be possible by using a control. Operating the control need not immediately start the equipment - control systems may require certain conditions (relating to operation or protection devices) to be met before starting can be achieved.

151 Restarting after any sort of stoppage is subject to the same requirement. The stop may have been deliberate, or may have happened, for example by the activation of a protection device. Restarting of the equipment should not be possible by the re-setting of a protection device such as an interlock, or a person's withdrawal from an area covered by a sensing device; operation of the start control should also be needed.

152 Any change in the operating conditions should only be possible by the use of a control, except if the change does not increase risk to health or safety. Examples of operating conditions include speed, pressure, temperature and power.

153 The purpose of regulation 14(1)(b), together with 14(2), is to ensure that users or other people are not caught unawares by any changes in the operating conditions or modes of the equipment in use. For example, certain multi-functional machines are used in the metal-working industry for punching or shearing metal via different tools located on different parts of the machines. Safety in the use of these machines is achieved by means of a combination of safe systems of work and physical safeguards which match the characteristics of the workpiece. It is essential that the function of the machine (eg punching or shearing) is changed by means of a conscious, positive action by the operator and that unused parts of the machine cannot start up unintentionally. Another example of this type of machine is multi-functional combination machines used in woodworking. Similarly, unexpected increases in speed, pressure etc could expose operators to risk, for example when using power drills.

154 Regulation 14(3) acknowledges that in the case of automatic machinery, for example those controlled by programmable electronic systems, it is not appropriate to require separate controls for changing operating conditions

when such changes are part of the normal operating cycle. (Nevertheless these machines should be safeguarded as required by regulations 11 and 12). However, where interventions have to be made outside the normal sequence, such as clearing blockages, setting, or cleaning, controls should be provided in accordance with regulations 14(1) and (2).

155   The start control can be separate or combined with operating conditions controls, or more than one of each type of control can be provided. The controls do not have to be provided solely for the purpose of each Regulation and can be combined with other function controls such as stop controls required by regulation 15, although not with an emergency stop control provided in accordance with regulation 16. 'Hold-to-run' devices are examples of combined stop and start controls. These should be designed so that the stop function has priority, following the release of the control.

156   The controls provided should be designed and positioned so as to prevent, so far as possible, inadvertent or accidental operation. Buttons and levers should be of appropriate design, for example including a shrouding or locking facility. It should not be possible for the control to 'operate itself', such as due to the effects of gravity, vibration, or failure of a spring mechanism. Starting initiated from a keyboard or other multi-function device should require a confirmatory input in addition to the start command. Furthermore, the results of the actuation should be displayed.

Regulation 15   Stop controls

-(1)   Every employer shall ensure that, where appropriate, work equipment is provided with one or more readily accessible controls the operation of which will bring the work equipment to a safe condition in a safe manner.

(2)   Any control required by paragraph (1) shall bring the work equipment to a complete stop where necessary for reasons of health and safety.

(3)   Any control required by paragraph (1) shall, if necessary for reasons of health and safety, switch off all sources of energy after stopping the functioning of the work equipment.

(4)   Any control required by paragraph (1) shall operate in priority to any control which starts or changes the operating conditions of the work equipment.

157   The primary requirement of this Regulation is that the action of the control should bring the equipment to a safe condition in a safe manner. This acknowledges that it is not always desirable to bring all items of work equipment immediately to a complete stop; for example, it would be unsafe to bring a self-contained hydraulic machine to a complete stop if doing so would cause it to collapse. Similarly, stopping the mixing mechanism of a reactor during certain chemical reactions could lead to a dangerous exothermic reaction.

158   Regulation 15(2) is qualified by 'where necessary for reasons of health and safety'. Therefore accessible dangerous parts must be rendered stationary. However, parts of equipment which do not present a risk, such as suitably guarded cooling fans, do not need to be positively stopped and may be allowed to idle.

159 The stop control does not have to be instantaneous in its action and can bring the equipment to rest in sequence or at the end of an operating cycle if this is required for safety. This may be necessary in some processes, for example to prevent the unsafe build-up of heat or pressure, to allow a controlled run-down of large rotating parts with high inertia.

160 Regulation 15(3) requires that the control should switch off all sources of energy from the equipment, after it has stopped, if this is necessary to prevent or minimise risk to health or safety. As the requirement is to minimise risk, the control should be arranged to switch off all energy sources unless this would actually increase the risk. That could be the case where materials are held by a magnetic clutch or grab, or where power is needed for restraint to prevent collapse or other uncontrolled movement. In such cases, power should be retained so as to ensure safety, and if necessary an appropriate system of work should be employed subsequently to isolate the equipment from its power source. Where it is necessary to retain power for production reasons and a hazard could arise due to unexpected movement giving rise to risk of injury, control systems should be designed so as to immediately remove the power should such an event occur.

161 Where internally stored energy could lead to risk, it should be cut off by the action of the stop control. For example, horizontal plastic injection moulding machines may store hydraulic energy in internal hydraulic reservoirs which, under certain fault conditions, may cause uncovenanted movements which could cause injury. In this case, the stop control should effectively isolate or dissipate the stored energy so as to ensure safety.

162 The stop control should override the effect of any operating or start control. Where possible it should not require anything other than a short manual action to activate it, even though the stop and disconnection sequence so initiated may take some time to complete.

163 Further information on the categories of stop functions can be found in BS EN 60204-1. Although this standard applies to new machinery, it gives guidance which may be useful for any equipment.

15

Regulation 16

Emergency stop controls

-(1) Every employer shall ensure that, where appropriate, work equipment is provided with one or more readily accessible emergency stop controls unless it is not necessary by reason of the nature of the hazards and the time taken for the work equipment to come to a complete stop as a result of the action of any control provided by virtue of regulation 15(1).

(2) Any control required by paragraph (1) shall operate in priority to any control required by regulation 15(1).

164 An emergency stop control should be provided where the other safeguards are not adequate to prevent risk when some irregular event occurs. However, an emergency stop control should not be considered as a substitute for necessary safeguarding. Examples of such situations include: a person becoming exposed to a hazard; or the failure or malfunction of a machine generating additional hazards (eg overspeeding, failure to stop). However, if such an event can happen very quickly, (eg failure of the protection system at a hand-fed power-operated guillotine), it is unlikely that an emergency stop

would be of benefit since people would have no time to react; it would not then be appropriate to provide an emergency stop control.

165 When it is appropriate to have one, an emergency stop should be provided at every control point and at other appropriate locations around the equipment so that action can be taken quickly. The location of emergency stop controls should be determined as a follow-up to the risk assessment.

166 Although it is desirable that emergency stops rapidly bring work equipment to a halt, this must be achieved under control so as not to create an additional hazard.

167 Emergency stops are intended to effect a rapid response to potentially dangerous situations and they should not be used as functional stops during normal operation.

168 Emergency stop controls should be easily reached and actuated. Common types are mushroom-headed buttons, bars, levers, kick-plates, or pressure-sensitive cables. Guidance on specific features of emergency stops is given in national and international standards (BS EN 292, BS 5304, prEN 418, BS EN 60204-1).

Regulation 17   Controls

-(1) Every employer shall ensure that all controls for work equipment shall be clearly visible and identifiable, including by appropriate marking where necessary.

(2) Except where necessary, the employer shall ensure that no control for work equipment is in a position where any person operating the control is exposed to a risk to his health or safety.

(3) Every employer shall ensure where appropriate-

(a) that, so far as is reasonably practicable, the operator of any control is able to ensure from the position of that control that no person is in a place where he would be exposed to any risk to his health or safety as a result of the operation of that control, but where or to the extent that it is not reasonably practicable;

(b) that, so far as is reasonably practicable, systems of work are effective to ensure that, when work equipment is about to start, no person is in a place where he would be exposed to a risk to his health or safety as a result of the work equipment starting, but where neither of these is reasonably practicable;

(c) that an audible, visible or other suitable warning is given by virtue of regulation 24 whenever work equipment is about to start.

(4) Every employer shall take appropriate measures to ensure that any person who is in a place where he would be exposed to a risk to his health or safety as a result of the starting or stopping of work equipment has sufficient time and suitable means to avoid that risk.

Regulation 17(1)

169 It should be possible to identify easily what each control does and on which equipment it takes effect. Both the controls and their markings should be clearly visible. As well as having legible wording or symbols, factors such as the colour, shape and position of controls are important; a combination of these can often be used to reduce ambiguity. Some controls may need to be distinguishable by touch, for example inching buttons on printing machines. Few controls will be adequately identifiable without marking of some sort.

170 The marking and form of many controls is covered by national and international standards (BS 3641, prEN 50099). However, additional marking may often be desirable.

Regulation 17(2)

171 Controls used in the normal running of the equipment should not be placed where anybody using them might be exposed to risk. However, controls used for setting-up and fault-finding procedures may have to be positioned where people are at some risk, for example on a robot-teaching pendant. In such cases particular precautions should be employed to ensure safety; examples include using hold-to-run controls, enabling controls, emergency stop controls. Further precautions include the selection of reduced/limited capability of the work equipment during such operations.

Regulation 17(3)(a)

172 The provisions of regulation 17(3)(a) apply where physical safeguarding methods employed in accordance with regulation 11(2)(a) and (b) do not completely prevent access to dangerous parts of work equipment, or where people are at risk from other aspects of the operation, eg noise, or harmful radiation. The preferred aim is to position controls so that operators of equipment are able to see from the control position that no-one is at risk from anything they set going. To be able to do this, operators need to have a view of any part of the equipment that may put anyone at risk. A direct view is best, but supplementing by mirrors or more sophisticated visual or sensing facilities may be necessary.

173 There will normally be little difficulty in meeting this requirement in the case of small and compact equipment. With larger equipment there is normally some latitude in the positioning of controls, and the safety aspect should be considered in deciding their location; this would apply for example on large process plant such as newspaper printing machinery or chemical plant.

174 Where people are at risk from dangerous parts of machinery, normal safeguarding procedures should restrict the need for surveillance to vulnerable areas; an example would be on large newspaper printing machines. However, where regular intervention is necessary which involves entry into, removal of, or opening of safeguards, (eg for maintenance purposes), interlocks or similar devices should be employed to prevent start-up while people are at risk. It may be necessary to employ additional measures to ensure that people do not remain inside safeguards at start-up. Similarly, where sensing devices are employed to aid surveillance, they may be interlocked with the controls so as to prevent start-up when people are at risk.

175 If anyone other than the operator also attend the equipment, they may have permissive start controls located at a position of safety from where they can ascertain that no-one is at risk. Such controls can indicate to the operator that everyone is clear and permit a start.

176 Where the risk is from hazards other than dangerous parts of machinery (eg noise, radiation), people at some distance from the work equipment may be at risk. In such circumstances the means of compliance with regulation 17(3) should depend upon the nature and extent of the risk. It may not always be reasonably practicable for operators to have sight of all parts of the workplace that may be affected by such 'widespread risks'; so it may be necessary in such cases to employ systems of work or warning devices. In the latter case warning devices should be selected critically depending on the risk; for example, it would not be acceptable to rely on audible or visible alarms where the risk is of an imminent potentially fatal dose of ionising radiation, but they may be adequate where the risk is from noisy plant.

Regulation 17(3)(b)

177 If the nature of the installation is such that it is not reasonably practicable for the operator at the control position to ensure that no-one is at risk, then a system of work must be devised and used to achieve that aim. This should set out procedures to eliminate or reduce the probability of any workers being at risk as a result of starting-up. An example is the use of systems using signallers; these are often used to assist crane drivers, or tractor drivers setting a manned harvester in motion. As far as possible, the system of work should lay down procedures to be followed by those concerned with the use of the equipment, rather than placing responsibilities on others peripherally involved, such as people walking through the area.

Regulation 17(3)(c)

178 The warning should comply with regulation 24, ie it should be unambiguous, easily perceived and easily understood.

179 Circumstances will affect the type of warning chosen. Some general comments about warnings are made under regulation 24. Signals which are not audible and visual may be suitable (eg tactile signals). Often a combination of signals affecting different senses may be appropriate.

Regulation 17(4)

180 Warnings given in accordance with regulation 17(3)(c), should be given sufficiently in advance of the equipment actually starting to give those at risk time to get clear. As well as time, suitable means of avoiding the risk should be provided. This may take the form of a device by means of which the person at risk can prevent start-up or warn the operator of his/her presence. Otherwise there must be adequate provision to enable people at risk to withdraw, eg sufficient space or exits.

181 The provisions of regulation 17 do not preclude people from remaining in positions where they are at risk. Their aim is to prevent an operator unintentionally placing people at risk. Regulation 11, in its hierarchical approach to safeguarding, recognises that in exceptional circumstances people may have to approach dangerous parts of machinery, such as for maintenance purposes. Access to such positions should only be allowed under strictly controlled conditions and in accordance with regulation 11.

Regulation 18

Control systems

-(1) Every employer shall ensure, so far as is reasonably practicable, that all control systems of work equipment are safe.

(2) Without prejudice to the generality of paragraph(1), a control system shall not be safe unless-

(a) its operation does not create any increased risk to health or safety;

(b) it ensures, so far as is reasonably practicable, that any fault in or damage to any part of the control system or the loss of supply of any source of energy used by the work equipment cannot result in additional or increased risk to health or safety;

(c) it does not impede the operation of any control required by regulation 15 or 16.

182   A more complete definition of a control system than that given in paragraph 148 is:

a control system is a system or device which responds to input signals and generates an output signal which causes the equipment under control to operate in a particular manner.

183   The input signals may be from an operator via a manual control, or from the equipment itself, for example from automatic sensors or protection devices (photo-electric guards, guard interlock devices, speed limiters, etc). Signals from the equipment may also include information (feedback) on the condition of the equipment and its response (eg position, whether running, speed).

184   Failure of any part of the control system or its power supply should lead to a 'fail-safe' condition (more correctly and realistically called 'minimised failure to danger'), and not impede the operation of the 'stop' or 'emergency stop' controls. The measures which should be taken in the design and application of a control system to mitigate against the effects its failure will need to be balanced against the consequences of any failure. The greater the risk, the more resistant the control system should be to the effects of failure.

185   There are national and international standards both current and in preparation (BS 5304, BS EN 60204-1, BS 6491) which provide guidance on design of control systems so as to achieve high levels of performance related to safety.

Regulation 19

Isolation from sources of energy

-(1) Every employer shall ensure that where appropriate work equipment is provided with suitable means to isolate it from all its sources of energy.

(2) Without prejudice to the generality of paragraph (1), the means mentioned in that paragraph shall not be suitable unless they are clearly identifiable and readily accessible.

(3) Every employer shall take appropriate measures to ensure that re-connection of any energy source to work equipment does not expose any person using the work equipment to any risk to his health or safety.

Figure 2 Multi-padlockable hasp for locking off isolating valve

186 Isolation means establishing a break in the energy supply in a secure manner, ie by ensuring that inadvertent reconnection is not possible. The possibilities and risks of reconnection should be identified as part of the risk assessment, which should then establish how security can be achieved. For some equipment, this can be achieved by simply removing the plug from the electrical supply socket. For other equipment, an isolating switch or valve may have to be locked in the off or closed position to avoid unsafe reconnection. The closed position is not always the safe position: for example, drain or vent outlets may need to be secured in the open position. If work on isolated equipment is being done by more than one person, it may be necessary to provide a locking device with multiple locks and keys; each will have their own lock or key, and all locks have to be taken off before the isolating device can be removed (see Figure 2).

187 The main aim of this Regulation is to allow equipment to be made safe under particular circumstances, such as when maintenance is to be carried out, when an unsafe condition develops (failure of a component, overheating, or pressure build-up), or where a temporarily adverse environment would render the equipment unsafe, for example electrical equipment in wet conditions or in a flammable or explosive atmosphere.

188 There may be some circumstances in which, for particular safety reasons, stopping equipment does not remove all sources of energy, ie the power supply is helping to keep the equipment safe. In such cases, isolation could lead to consequent danger, so it will be necessary to take appropriate measures to overcome that risk before attempting to isolate the equipment.

189 It is appropriate to provide means of isolation where the work equipment is dependent upon external energy sources such as electricity, pressure

(hydraulic or pneumatic) or heat. Internal energy which is an inherent part of the materials from which the equipment is made, such as its potential energy, chemical or radiological energy, similarly cannot be isolated from the equipment; nevertheless there should be means of preventing such energy adversely affecting workers, by restraint, barrier or shielding.

190   Electrical isolation of electrical equipment for work on or near conductors is dealt with by regulation 12 of the Electricity at Work Regulations 1989. Guidance to those Regulations expands on the means of isolating electrical equipment. Note that those Regulations are only concerned with electrical danger (electric shock or burn, arcing and fire or explosion caused by electricity), and do not deal with other hazards (such as mechanical) that may arise from failure to isolate electrical equipment.

191   Heat energy may be supplied by circulation of pre-heated fluid such as water or steam. In such cases, isolating valves should be fitted to the supply pipework. Similar provision should be made for energy supplies in the form of liquids or gases under pressure. The performance of such valves may deteriorate over time, and their effectiveness often cannot be judged visually. A planned preventive maintenance programme should therefore be instigated which assures effective means of isolation.

192   The energy source of some equipment is held in the substances contained within it. Examples are the use of gases or liquids as fuel, electrical accumulators (batteries) and radionuclides. In such cases, isolation may mean removing the energy-containing material, although this may not always be necessary.

193   Also, it is clearly not appropriate to isolate the terminals of a battery from the chemical cells within it, since that could not be done without destroying the whole unit.

194   Some equipment makes use of natural sources of energy such as light or flowing water. In such cases suitable means of isolation include screening from light, and the means of diverting water flow respectively. Another natural energy source, wind power, is less easily diverted, so sail mechanisms should be designed and constructed so as to permit minimal energy transfer when necessary.

195   Regulation 19(3) requires precautions to ensure that people are not put at risk following reconnection of the energy source. So, reconnection of the energy source should not put people at risk by itself initiating movement or other hazard. Measures are also required to ensure that guards and other protection devices are functioning correctly before operation begins.

Regulation 20   Stability

Every employer shall ensure that work equipment or any part of work equipment is stabilised by clamping or otherwise where necessary for purposes of health or safety.

196   There are many types of work equipment that might fall over, collapse or overturn unless suitable precautions are taken to fix them to the ground, stabilise them, tie, fasten or clamp them in some way.

Fixed work equipment

197   Most machines used in a fixed position should be bolted or otherwise fastened down so that they do not move or rock during use. It has long been recognised that woodworking and other machines (except those specifically designed for portable use) should be bolted to the floor or similarly secured to prevent unexpected movement.

198   The measures can be by fastening the equipment to an appropriate foundation or supporting structure. Other means could include lashing or tying to a supporting structure or platform.

199   Where the stability of work equipment is not inherent in its design or operation or where it is mounted in a position where its stability could be compromised, eg by severe weather conditions, then additional measures should be taken to ensure its stability. Scaffolds are vulnerable to strong winds and therefore sheeting and additional ties will be needed.

200   Ladders should be at the correct angle height and tied or footed. Mobile tower scaffolds should not be so high that they become unstable and should be tied to the building and be anchored or have the base appropriately extended by fitting outriggers.

Mobile work equipment

201   Some types of work equipment may need counterbalance weights to balance loads at either the front or the rear (eg tractors). Mobile cranes are fitted with a wide range of devices to increase stability.

202   Additional measures may be needed for particular applications. Wherever lift trucks are used the type selected should be suitable for the terrain over which it may travel.

203   Certain types of mobile equipment, for example mobile cranes or access platforms, while inherently stable when not lifting, can have their stability increased during use by means of outriggers or similar devices. While this equipment cannot be 'clamped' or 'fixed' steps must be taken to ensure that the equipment is always used within the limits of its stability at any given time.

Regulation 21

Lighting

Every employer shall ensure that suitable and sufficient lighting, which takes account of the operations to be carried out, is provided at any place where a person uses work equipment.

204   Any place where a person uses work equipment should be suitably and sufficiently lit. If the ambient lighting provided in the workplace is suitable and sufficient for the tasks involved in the use of the equipment then special lighting need not be provided. But if the task involves the perception of detail, for example precision measurements, then additional lighting would need to be provided to comply with the Regulation. The lighting should be adequate for the needs of the task.

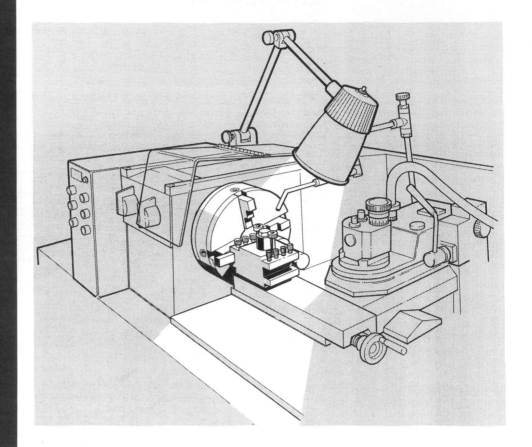

Figure 3 Local lighting

205 Local lighting on the machine for the illumination of the work area should be provided when the construction of the machine and/or its guards render the normal lighting inadequate for the safe and efficient operation of the machine, eg on sewing machines. Local lighting may be needed to give sufficient view of a dangerous process or to reduce visual fatigue (see Figure 3).

206 Additional lighting should also be provided in areas not covered by general lighting when work, such as maintenance or repairs, for example, is carried out in them. The arrangements for the provision of lighting could be temporary, by means of hand or other portable lights, eg miners' lamps, or by fixed lighting inside enclosures, such as lift shafts. The standard of lighting required will be related to the purpose for which the work equipment is used or to the work being carried out.

207 Where access is foreseeable on an intermittent but regular basis, consideration should always be given to the provision of permanent lighting.

208 This Regulation complements the requirement for sufficient and suitable workplace lighting in the Workplace (Health, Safety and Welfare) Regulations 1992. Practical advice is contained in HSE guidance HS(G)38.

21

Regulation 22   Maintenance operations

Regulation
22

Every employer shall take appropriate measures to ensure that work equipment is so constructed or adapted that, so far as is reasonably practicable, maintenance operations which involve a risk to health or safety can be carried out while the work equipment is shut down or, in other cases -

> *(a) maintenance operations can be carried out without exposing the person carrying them out to a risk to his health or safety; or*

> *(b) appropriate measures can be taken for the protection of any person carrying out maintenance operations which involve a risk to his health or safety.*

209   Regulation 6 requires that equipment is maintained. Regulation 22 requires that equipment is constructed or adapted in a way that takes account of the risks associated with carrying out maintenance work, such as routine and planned preventive maintenance, as described in the guidance to regulation 6. Compliance with this Regulation will help to ensure that when maintenance work is carried out, it is possible to do it safely and without risk to health, as required by Section 2 of the HSW Act; it will also help to comply with regulation 5(1), since 'used' includes maintained. Regulation 11(3)(h) contains a requirement linked to regulation 22, but focusing on the narrower aspect of the design of guards for such work. Many accidents have occurred during maintenance work, often as a result of failure to adapt the equipment to reduce the risk.

210   In some cases the need for safe maintenance will have been considered at the design stage and attended to by the manufacturer, and the user will need to do little other than review the measures provided. In other cases, particularly when a range of interconnecting components may be put together, eg in a research laboratory or a production line, users of the equipment will need to consider when carrying out their risk assessment (paragraph 16) whether any extra features need be incorporated so that maintenance can be done safely and without risks to health.

211   Ideally there is no risk associated with the maintenance operation. For example, lubrication points on machines may be designed so that they can be used safely even while the machine is in motion, or adjustment points positioned so that they can be used without opening guards.

212   If, however, the maintenance work might involve a risk, this Regulation requires that the installation should be designed so that the work can, so far as is reasonably practicable, be carried out with the equipment stopped or inactive. This will probably be the case for most equipment.

213   If equipment will have to be running or working during a maintenance operation and this presents risks, measures should be taken to enable the operation of the equipment in a way that reduces the risk. These measures include further safeguards or functions designed into the equipment, such as limiting the power, speed or range of movement that is available to dangerous parts during maintenance operations. Examples are:

(a)   providing temporary guards;

(b)   limited movement controls;

(c)   crawl speed operated by hold-to-run controls;

(d)   using a second low-powered visible laser beam to align a powerful invisible one.

214   Other measures that can be taken to protect against any residual risk include wearing personal protective equipment and provision of instruction and

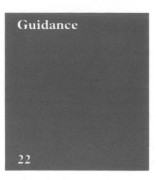

supervision. Although the actual use of these measures falls outside the scope of this Regulation, the work equipment should as far as possible be installed to be compatible with their use.

215 The design of equipment in relation to maintenance work on it may also be affected by other legislation. In particular, electrically powered equipment is subject to the Electricity at Work Regulations 1989 as regards risks of injury from electric shock or burn, or from explosion or ignition initiated by electricity. Guidance on those Regulations includes details of relevant equipment requirements.

Regulation 23

Markings

Every employer shall ensure that work equipment is marked in a clearly visible manner with any marking appropriate for reasons of health and safety.

216 This Regulation is closely related to the following one which deals with warnings; some markings may also serve as the warning required by regulation 24. There are many circumstances in which marking of equipment is appropriate for health or safety reasons. Stop and start controls for equipment need to be identified. The maximum rotation speed of an abrasive wheel should be marked upon it. The maximum safe working load should be marked on lifting beams. Gas cylinders should indicate (normally by colour) the gas in them. Storage and feed vessels containing hazardous substances should generally be marked to show their contents, and any hazard associated with them.

217 Some legislation lays down specific circumstances in which markings are needed, and what form they should take. Examples of Regulations requiring particular markings are Ionising Radiation Regulations 1985, and the Highly Flammable Liquids Regulations 1972 (regulations 6 to 7). Pressure vessels are subject to various Regulations, which include requirements for marking the vessel with specific information.

218 Employers should consider any other marking that might be appropriate for their own purposes, eg numbering machines to aid identification, particularly if the controls or isolators for the machines are not directly attached to them and there could otherwise be confusion.

219 Markings may use words, letters, numbers, or symbols, and the use of colour or shape may be significant. There are nationally or internationally agreed markings relating to some hazards, eg the international symbols for radiation and lasers. Markings should as far as possible conform to such published standards as BS 5378 or as required by any appropriate legislation such as the Safety Signs Regulations 1980.

Regulation 24

Warnings

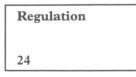

-*(1) Every employer shall ensure that work equipment incorporates any warnings or warning devices which are appropriate for reasons of health and safety.*

(2) Without prejudice to the generality of paragraph (1), warnings given by

warning devices on work equipment shall not be appropriate unless they are unambiguous, easily perceived and easily understood.

220   Warnings or warning devices may be appropriate where risks to health or safety remain after other hardware measures have been taken. They may be incorporated into systems of work (including permit-to-work systems), and can reinforce measures of information, instruction and training. A warning is normally in the form of a notice or similar. Examples are positive instructions ('hard hats must be worn'), prohibitions ('not to be operated by people under 18 years'), restrictions ('do not heat above 60°C'). A warning device is an active unit giving a signal; the signal may typically be visible or audible, and is often connected into equipment so that it is active only when a hazard exists.

221   In some cases, warnings and warning devices will be specified in other legislation, for example automatic safe load indicators on mobile cranes on construction sites, or 'X-rays on' lights.

Warnings

222   Warnings can be permanent printed ones; these may be attached to or incorporated into the equipment or positioned close to it. There may also be a need for portable warnings to be posted during temporary operations such as maintenance; these may form part of a permit-to-work system.

223   In some cases words can be augmented or replaced by appropriate graphical signs. So as to be readily understood, such signs will normally need to be from a nationally or internationally agreed standard set. The Safety Signs Regulations 1980 are relevant here.

Warning devices

224   Warning devices can be audible (eg reversing alarms on construction vehicles) or visible (eg a light on a control panel that a fan on a microbiological cabinet has broken down or a blockage has occurred on a particular machine). They may indicate imminent danger (eg machine about to start), development of a fault condition (eg pump failure or conveyor blockage indicator on a control panel) or the continued presence of a potential hazard (eg hot-plate or laser on). A particular warning may use both types of device simultaneously, for example some automatic safe load indicators on mobile cranes.

225   They must be easily perceived and understood, and unambiguous. It is important to consider factors which affect people's perception of such devices, especially for warnings of imminent danger. Visual warnings will be effective only if a person frequently looks in a particular direction, and therefore may not be as widely applicable as audible signals. Appropriate choice of colour and flashing can catch attention, and also reinforce the warning nature of a visual signal. The sound given by an audible signal should be of such a type that people unambiguously perceive it as a warning. This means that it must be possible to distinguish between the warnings given by separate warning devices and between the warnings and any other, unrelated, signals which may be in operation at the time. It may not be possible to rely on audible signals in a noisy environment, nor in circumstances where many such signals are expected to be active at one time.

Regulation 25

Exemption certificates

   -(1)   The Secretary of State for Defence may, in the interests of national security, by a certificate in writing exempt any of the home forces, any visiting force or

any headquarters from any of the requirements of these Regulations and any such exemption may be granted subject to conditions and to a limit of time and may be revoked by the said Secretary of State by a further certificate in writing at any time.

    (2)   In this regulation –

    (a)   "the home forces" has the same meaning as in section 12(1) of the Visiting Forces Act 1952[(a)];

    (b)   "headquarters" has the same meaning as in article 3(2) of the Visiting Forces and International Headquarters (Application of Law) Order 1965[(b)];

    (c)   "visiting force" has the same meaning as it does for the purposes of any provision of Part I of the Visiting Forces Act 1952.

(a) 1952 C.67.
(b) S.I. 1965/1536, to which there are amendments not relevant to these regulations.

Regulation 26

Extension outside Great Britain

Regulation

    These Regulations shall, subject to regulation 3, apply to and in relation to the premises and activities outside Great Britain to which sections 1 to 59 and 80 to 82 of the 1974 Act apply by virtue of the Health and Safety at Work etc. Act 1974 (Application outside Great Britain) Order 1989[(a)] as they apply within Great Britain.

(a) S.I. 1989/840.

Guidance 26

226 The Regulations apply to offshore activities covered by the 1989 Order on or associated with oil and gas installations, including mobile installations, diving support vessels, heavy lift barges and pipe-lay barges.

Regulation 27

Repeals, saving and revocations

Regulation

    -(1)   Subject to paragraph (2) the enactments mentioned in Part I of Schedule 2 are repealed to the extent specified in column 3 of that Part.

    (2)   Nothing in this regulation shall affect the operation of any provision of the Offices, Shops and Railway Premises Act 1963[(a)] as that provision has effect by virtue of section 90(4) of that Act.

    (3)   The instruments mentioned in Part II of Schedule 2 are revoked to the extent specified in column 3 of that Part.

(a) 1963 c. 41.

Guidance

227 The Regulations replace many existing laws, particularly on machinery guarding, by repealing and revoking old and in many cases obsolescent legislation.

228 Existing legislation listed in Schedule 2 for repeal or revocation will continue to operate alongside the new Regulations until 1 January 1997, and will apply as explained in the guidance to regulation 1.

Schedule 1

Relevant Community Directives

Regulation 10

1   Council Directive 73/23/EEC on the harmonization of the laws of Member States relating to electrical equipment designed for use within certain voltage limits (OJ No. L77, 26.3.1973, p.29)

2   Council Directive of 79/113/EEC on the approximation of the laws of the Member States relating to the determination of the noise emission of construction plant and equipment (OJ No. L33, 8.2.1979, p.15)

3   Council Directive 81/1051/EEC amending Directive 79/113/EEC on the approximation of the laws of the Member States relating to the determination of the noise emission of construction plant and equipment (OJ No. L376, 30.12.1981, p.49)

4   Council Directive 84/532/EEC on the approximation of the laws of the Member States relating to common provisions for construction plant and equipment (OJ No. L300, 19.11.1984, p.111)

5   Council Directive 84/533/EEC on the approximation of the laws of the Member States relating to the permissible sound power level of compressors (OJ No. L300, 19.11.1984, p.123)

6   Council Directive 84/534/EEC on the approximation of the laws of the Member States relating to the permissible sound power level of tower cranes (OJ No. L300, 19.11.1984, p.130)

7   Council Directive 84/535/EEC on the approximation of the laws of the Member States relating to the permissible sound power level of welding generators (OJ No. L300, 19.11.1984, p.142)

8   Council Directive 84/536/EEC on the approximation of the laws of the Member States relating to the permissible sound power level of power generators (OJ No. L300, 19.11.1984, p.149)

9   Council Directive 84/537/EEC on the approximation of the laws of the Member States relating to the permissible sound power level of powered hand-held concrete-breakers and picks (OJ No. L300, 19.11.1984, p.156)

10   Council Directive 84/538/EEC on the approximation of the laws of the Member States relating to the permissible sound power level of lawnmowers (OJ No. L300, 19.11.1984, p.171)

11   Commission Directive 84/405/EEC adapting to technical progress Council Directive 79/113/EEC on the approximation of the laws of the Member States relating to the determination of the noise emission of construction plant and equipment (OJ No. L233, 30.8.1985, p.9)

12   Commission Directive 85/406/EEC adapting to technical progress Council Directive 84/533/EEC on the approximation of the laws of the Member States relating to the permissible sound power level of compressors (OJ No. L233, 30.8.1985, p.11)

13   Commission Directive 85/407/EEC adapting to technical progress Council Directive 84/535/EEC on the approximation of the laws of the Member States relating to the permissible sound power level of welding generators (OJ No. L233, 30.8.1985, p.16)

14   Commission Directive 85/408/EEC adapting to technical progress Council Directive 84/536/EEC on the approximation of the laws of the Member States relating to the permissible sound power level of power generators (OJ No. L233, 30.8.1985, p.18)

15   Commission Directive 85/409/EEC adapting to technical progress Council Directive 84/537/EEC on the approximation of the laws of the Member States relating to the permissible sound power level of powered hand-held concrete-breakers and picks (OJ No. L233, 30.8.1985, p.20)

16   Commission Directive 87/252/EEC adapting to technical progress Council Directive 84/538/EEC on the approximation of the laws of the Member States relating to the permissible sound power level of lawn mowers (OJ No. L117, 5.5.1987, p.22 with corrigenda at OJ No. L158, 18.6.1987, p.31)

17   Council Directive 87/405/EEC amending Directive 84/534/EEC on the laws of the Member States relating to the permissible sound power level of tower cranes (OJ No. L220, 8.8.1987, p.60)

18   Council Directive 88/180/EEC amending Directive 84/538/EEC on the approximation of the laws of the Member States relating to the permissible sound power level of lawnmowers (OJ No. L81, 26.3.1988, p.69)

19   Council Directive 88/181/EEC amending Directive 84/538/EEC on the approximation of the laws of the Member States relating to the permissible sound power level of lawnmowers (OJ No. L81, 26.3.1988, p.71)

20   Council Directive 84/539/EEC on the approximation of the laws of the Member States relating to electro-medical equipment used in human or veterinary medicine (OJ No. L300, 19.11.1984, p.179)

21   Council Directive 86/295/EEC on the approximation of the laws of the Member States relating to roll-over protective structures (ROPS) for certain construction plant (OJ No. L186, 8.7.1986, p.1)

22   Council Directive 86/296/EEC on the approximation of the laws of the Member States relating to falling-object protective structures (FOPS) for certain construction plant (OJ No. L186, 8.7.1986, p.10)

23   Council Directive 86/662/EEC on the limitation of noise emitted by hydraulic excavators, rope-operated excavators, dozers, loaders and excavator-loaders (OJ No. L384, 31.12.1986, p.1)

24   Council Directive 86/663/EEC on the approximation of the laws of the Member States relating to self-propelled industrial trucks (OJ No. L384, 31.12.1986, p.12)

25   Council Directive 87/404/EEC on the harmonization of the laws of the Member States relating to simple pressure vessels (OJ No. L220, 8.8.1987, p.48)

26   Council Directive 89/106/EEC on the approximation of laws, regulations and administrative provisions of the Member States relating to construction products (OJ No. L40, 11.2.1989, p.12)

27   Commission Directive 89/240/EEC adapting to technical progress Council Directive 86/663/EEC on the approximation of the laws of the Member States relating to self-propelled industrial trucks (OJ No. L100, 12.4.1989, p.1)

28   Council Directive 89/336/EEC on the approximation of the laws of the Member States relating to electromagnetic compatibility (OJ No. L139, 23.5.1989, p.19)

29   *Council Directive 89/392/EEC on the approximation of the laws of the Member States relating to machinery (OJ No. L183, 29.6.1989, p.9)*

30   *Commission Directive 89/514/EEC adapting to technical progress Council Directive 86/662/EEC on the limitation of noise emitted by hydraulic excavators, rope-operated excavators, dozers, loaders and excavator-loaders (OJ No. L253, 30.8.1989, p.35)*

31   *Council Directive 89/686/EEC on the approximation of the laws of the Member States relating to personal protective equipment (OJ No. L399, 30.12.1989, p.18)*

32   *Council Directive 90/385/EEC on the approximation of the laws of the Member States relating to active implantable medical devices (OJ No. L189, 20.7.1990, p.17)*

33   *Council Directive 90/396/EEC on the approximation of the laws of the Member States relating to appliances burning gaseous fuels (OJ No. L196, 26.7.1990, p.15)*

34   *Council Directive 91/368/EEC amending Directive 89/392/EEC on the approximation of the laws of the Member States relating to machinery (OJ No. L198, 22.7.1991, p.16)*

35   *Council Directive 92/31/EEC amending Directive 89/336/EEC on the approximation of the laws of the Member States relating to electromagnetic compatibility (OJ No. L126, 12.5.92, p.11)*

229   Listed below is the implementing Regulations for each relevant Community Directive. The Regulations are listed in the same order as the Directives.

1   The Low Voltage Electrical Equipment (Safety) Regulations 1989 (SI 1989/728) HMSO ISBN 0 11 096728 3

2   The Construction Plant and Equipment (Harmonisation of Noise Emission Standards) Regulations 1985 (SI 1985/1968) HMSO ISBN 0 11 057968 2

     The Construction Plant and Equipment (Harmonisation of Noise Emission Standards) Regulations 1988 (SI 1988/361) HMSO ISBN 0 11 086361 5

     The Falling-object Protective Structures for Construction Plant (EEC Requirements) Regulations 1988 (SI 1988/362) HMSO ISBN 0 11 086362 3

     The Roll-over Protective Structures for Construction Plant (EEC Requirements) Regulations 1988 (SI 1988/363) HMSO ISBN 0 11 086363 1

     The Construction Plant and Equipment (Harmonisation of Noise Emission Standards) (Amendment) Regulations 1989 (SI 1989/1127) HMSO ISBN 0 11 097127 2

     The Construction Plant and Equipment (Harmonisation of Noise Emission Standards) (Amendment) Regulations 1992 (SI 1992/488) HMSO ISBN 0 11 023488 X

3   As No 2

4   As No 2

5   The Construction Plant and Equipment (Harmonisation of Noise Emission Standards) Regulations 1985 (SI 1985/1968) HMSO ISBN 0 11 057968 2

6   The Construction Plant and Equipment (Harmonisation of Noise Emission Standards) Regulations 1985 (SI 1985/1968) HMSO ISBN 0 11 057968 2 and The Construction Plant and Equipment (Harmonisation of Noise Emission Standards) (Amendment) Regulations 1989 (SI 1989/1127) HMSO ISBN 0 11 097127 2

7   The Construction Plant and Equipment (Harmonisation of Noise Emission Standards) Regulations 1985 (SI 1985/1968) HMSO ISBN 0 11 057968 2

8   The Construction Plant and Equipment (Harmonisation of Noise Emission Standards) Regulations 1985 (SI 1985/1968) HMSO ISBN 0 11 057968 2

9   The Construction Plant and Equipment (Harmonisation of Noise Emission Standards) Regulations 1985 (SI 1985/1968) HMSO ISBN 0 11 057968 2

10   The Lawnmowers (Harmonisation of Noise Emission Standards) Regulations 1986 (SI 1986/1795) HMSO ISBN 0 11 067795 1

11   As No 2

12   The Construction Plant and Equipment (Harmonisation of Noise Emission Standards) Regulations 1985 (SI 1985/1968) HMSO ISBN 0 11 057968 2

13   The Construction Plant and Equipment (Harmonisation of Noise Emission Standards) Regulations 1985 (SI 1985/1968) HMSO ISBN 0 11 057968 2

14   The Construction Plant and Equipment (Harmonisation of Noise Emission Standards) Regulations 1985 (SI 1985/1968) HMSO ISBN 0 11 057968 2

15   The Construction Plant and Equipment (Harmonisation of Noise Emission Standards) Regulations 1985 (SI 1985/1968) HMSO ISBN 0 11 057968 2

16   The Lawnmowers (Harmonisation of Noise Emission Standards) (Amendment) Regulations 1987 (SI 1987/876) HMSO ISBN 0 11 076876 0

17   As No 6

18   The Lawnmowers (Harmonisation of Noise Emission Standards) Regulations 1992 (SI 1992/168) HMSO ISBN 0 11 023168 6

19   The Lawnmowers (Harmonisation of Noise Emission Standards) Regulations 1992 (SI 1992/168) HMSO ISBN 0 11 023168 6

1

20   The Electro-Medical Equipment (EEC Requirements) Regulations 1988 (SI 1988/1586) HMSO ISBN 0 11 087586 9

21   The Roll-over Protective Structures for Construction Plant (EEC Requirements) Regulations 1988 (SI 1988/363) HMSO ISBN 0 11 086363 1

22   The Falling-object Protective Structures for Construction Plant (EEC Requirements) Regulations 1988 (SI 1988/362) HMSO ISBN 0 11 086362 3

23   The Construction Plant and Equipment (Harmonisation of Noise Emission Standards) Regulations 1988 (SI 1988/361) HMSO ISBN 0 11 086361 5 and The Construction Plant and Equipment (Harmonisation of Noise Emission Standards) (Amendment) Regulations 1992 (SI 1992/488) HMSO ISBN 0 11 023488 X

24   The Self-Propelled Industrial Trucks (EEC) Requirements Regulations 1988 (SI 1988/1736) HMSO ISBN 0 11 087736 5 as amended by SI 1989/1035 ISBN 0 11 097035 7

25   The Simple Pressure Vessels (Safety) Regulations 1991 (SI 1991/2749) HMSO ISBN 0 11 015902 0

26   The Construction Products Regulations 1991 (SI 1991/1620) HMSO ISBN 0 11 014620 4

27   As No 24

28   The Electromagnetic Compatibility Regulations 1992 (SI 1992/2372) HMSO ISBN 0 11 025372 8

29   The proposed Machinery (Safety) Regulations 1992 (SI not yet known)

30   The Construction Plant and Equipment (Harmonisation of Noise Emission Standards) Regulations 1988 (SI 1988/361) HMSO ISBN 0 11 086361 5 and The Construction Plant and Equipment (Harmonisation of Noise Emission Standards) (Amendment) Regulations 1992 (SI 1992/488) HMSO ISBN 0 11 023488 X

31   The proposed Personal Protective Equipment (Safety) Regulations 1992 (SI not yet known)

32   The proposed Active Implantable Medical Devices Regulations 1992 (SI not yet known)

33   The Gas Appliances (Safety) Regulations 1992 (SI 1992/711) HMSO ISBN 0 11 025711 0

34   As No 29

35   As No 28

1

Schedule 2

Repeals and revocations

Regulation 27

Part I Repeals

(1) Chapter	(2) Short title	(3) Extent of repeal
1954 c.70	The Mines and Quarries Act 1954	Sections 81(1) and 82
1961 c.34	The Factories Act 1961	Sections 12 to 16, 17 and 19
1963 c.41	The Offices, Shops and Railway Premises Act 1963	Section 17

Part II Revocations

(1) Title	(2) Reference	(3) Extent of revocation
Regulations dated 17th October 1905 (The Spinning by Self-Acting Mules Regulations 1905)	S.R. & O. 1905/1103, amended by the Employment Act 1989 (c.38) section 29(5), Schedule 8	The whole Regulations
The Aerated Water Regulations 1921	S.R. & O. 1921/1932, amended by S.I. 1981/686	Regulations 1, 2 and 8
The Horizontal Milling Machines Regulations 1928	S.R. & O. 1928/548, amended by S.R. & O. 1934/207	The exemptions and regulations 2 to 7
The Operations at Unfenced Machinery Regulations 1938	S.R. & O. 1938/641, amended by S.R. & O. 1946/156 and S.I. 1976/955	The whole Regulations
The Jute (Safety, Health and Welfare) Regulations 1948	S.I. 1948/1696, to which there are amendments not relevant to these Regulations	Regulations 15, 27 and 28 and the First Schedule
The Iron and Steel Foundries Regulations 1953	S.I. 1953/1464, amended by S.I. 1974/1681 and S.I. 1981/1332	Regulation 5

Schedule	*(1)* Title	*(2)* Reference	*(3)* Extent of revocation
	The Agriculture (Power Take-Off) Regulations 1957	S.I. 1957/1386, amended by S.I. 1976/1247, S.I. 1981/1414 and S.I. 1991/1913	The whole Regulations
	The Agriculture (Circular Saws) Regulations 1959	S.I. 1959/427, amended by S.I. 1981/1414	(i) In regulation 1, in sub-paragraph (b), from the beginning to "and" where it first occurs; and sub-paragraph (c); (ii) regulations 3 and 4; (iii) in regulation 5(1), the words from "unless" to "or"; and (iv) Schedule 1
	The Agriculture (Stationary Machinery) Regulations 1959	S.I. 1959/1216, amended by S.I. 1976/1247 and S.I. 1981/1414	The whole Regulations
	The Agriculture (Threshers and Balers) Regulations 1960	S.I. 1960/1199, amended by S.I. 1976/1247 and S.I. 1981/1414	In the Schedule, paragraphs 2, 3, 6, 7, 8, 9, 10, 11, 12, 16 and 17
	The Shipbuilding and Ship Repairing Regulations 1960	S.I. 1960/1932, to which there are amendments not relevant to these Regulations	Regulation 67
	The Construction (General Provisions) Regulations 1961	S.I. 1961/1580, to which there are amendments not relevant to these Regulations	Regulations 42, 43 and 57
	The Agriculture (Field Machinery) Regulations 1962	S.I. 1962/1472, amended by S.I. 1976/1247 and S.I. 1981/1414	In the Schedule, paragraphs 2 to 6 and 15 to 19
	The Abrasive Wheels Regulations 1970	S.I. 1970/535	In regulation 3, paragraphs (2), (3) and (4); and regulations 4, 6 to 8, 10 to 16, 18 and 19

2

Schedule	(1) Title	(2) Reference	(3) Extent of revocation
	The Woodworking Machines Regulations 1974	S.I. 1974/903, amended by S.I. 1978/1126	In regulation 1, paragraphs (2) and (3); in regulation 2, the definitions of "cutters", "machine table", "narrow band sawing machine", "sawmill" and "squared stock"; in regulation 3, paragraph (2); regulations 5 to 9, 14 to 19, 21 to 38, and 40 to 43
	The Offshore Installations (Operational Safety, Health and Welfare) Regulations 1976	S.I. 1976/1019, which has effect as an existing statutory provision under the 1974 Act by virtue of section 1(1) of the Offshore Safety Act 1992 (c.15)	Regulations 10 and 12
2	The Agriculture (Power Take-off) (Amendment) Regulations 1991	S.I. 1991/1913	The whole Regulations

Appendix 1

Employers' duties from 1 January 1993

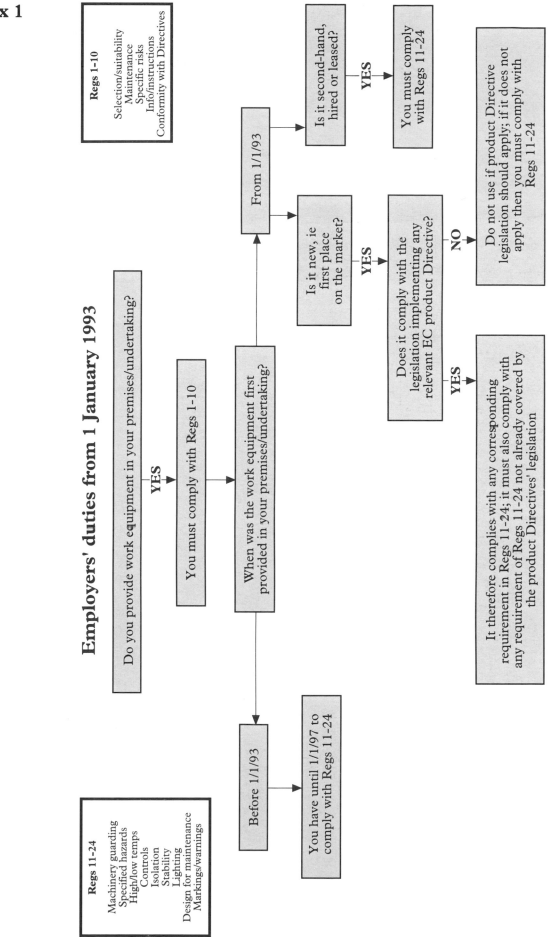

Regs 1-10
Selection/suitability
Maintenance
Specific risks
Info/instructions
Conformity with Directives

Regs 11-24
Machinery guarding
Specified hazards
High/low temps
Controls
Isolation
Stability
Lighting
Design for maintenance
Markings/warnings

Do you provide work equipment in your premises/undertaking?

YES

You must comply with Regs 1-10

When was the work equipment first provided in your premises/undertaking?

From 1/1/93

Before 1/1/93

You have until 1/1/97 to comply with Regs 11-24

Is it second-hand, hired or leased?

YES

You must comply with Regs 11-24

Is it new, ie first place on the market?

YES

Does it comply with the legislation implementing any relevant EC product Directive?

NO

Do not use if product Directive legislation should apply; if it does not apply then you must comply with Regs 11-24

YES

It therefore complies with any corresponding requirement in Regs 11-24; it must also comply with any requirement of Regs 11-24 not already covered by the product Directives' legislation

Appendix 2

Non-exhaustive list of existing legislation relevant to the Provision and Use of Work Equipment Regulations (PUWER)

Existing legislation	Key provisions to be replaced by PUWER*	Key provisions to be replaced by other legislation	Notes	What provisions of PUWER are particularly relevant?
The Health and Safety at Work etc Act 1974				ALL
The Factories Act 1961	12, 13, 14, 15, 16, 17, 19	1-7, 18, 24, 28, 29 57-60, 69, 72	20, 21, (young persons) and 22, 23, 25-27 (lifting equipment) will remain	ALL
The Mines and Quarries Act 1954	81(1), 82	93		ALL
The Offices, Shops and Railway Premises Act 1963	17	4-16, 23	18 (young persons) and 19 (training) will remain	ALL

* See guidance under Regulations 1 and 27 for details of the timetable for the repeal/revocation of these provisions

Existing legislation	Key provisions to be replaced by PUWER*	Key provisions to be replaced by other legislation	Notes	What provisions of PUWER are particularly relevant?
The Abrasive Wheels Regulations 1970	3(2), (3) and (4), 4, 6-8, 10-16, 18-19	17	9 (Training) and the Schedule will remain	ALL
The Aerated Waters Regulations 1921	1, 2, 8	3-5, 7, 9	All provisions will be revoked	5, 12
The Agriculture (Circular Saws) Regulations 1959	3, 4 Schedule 1			5, 6, 8, 11, 12, 21
The Agriculture (Power Take-off) Regulations 1957 (as amended)	All			11
The Agriculture (Stationary Machinery) Regulations 1959	All			5, 6, 11, 15, 16, 17, 21
The Agriculture (Threshers and Balers) Regulations 1960	In the Schedule paras 2, 3, 6, 7, 8, 9, 10, 11, 12, 16 and 17			5, 6, 11, 15, 16, 17, 21
The Agriculture (Field Machinery) Regulations 1962	In the Schedule Paras 2-6, 15-19			5, 6, 11, 15, 16
The Agriculture (Tractor Cabs) Regulations 1974				5
The Construction (General Provisions) Regulations 1961	42, 43, 57	55		5, 6, 11, 12, 21
The Construction (Lifting Operations) Regulations 1961				5, 6, 9, 14, 20, 23, 24

* See guidance under Regulations 1 and 27 for details of the timetable for the repeal/revocation of these provisions

Existing legislation	Key provisions to be replaced by PUWER*	Key provisions to be replaced by other legislation	Notes	What provisions of PUWER are particularly relevant?
The Construction (Working Places) Regulations 1966				5, 6, 9, 20
The Docks Regulations 1988				ALL
The Electricity at Work Regulations 1989				ALL
The Health and Safety (Display Screen Equipment) Regulations 1992			Implements Article 118A Directive	ALL
The Horizontal Milling Machines Regulations 1928	The Exemptions, 2-7	1	All provisions will be revoked	5, 6, 10, 11, 14, 15, 17, 21
The Iron and Steel Foundries Regulations 1953	5	4, 6, 8,9	All provisions will be revoked	6, 13
The Jute (Safety, Health and Welfare) Regulations 1948	15, 27, 28 1st Schedule	11, 13, 14-16, 19-26		5, 6, 8, 9, 11, 12, 13, 21, 22
The Management of Health and Safety at Work Regulations 1992			Implements Article 118A Directive	ALL
The Manual Handling Operations Regulations 1992			Implements Article 118A Directive	ALL
The Offshore Installations (Operational Safety, Health and Welfare) Regulations 1976	10, 12			5, 6, 20, 23, 24

* See guidance under Regulations 1 and 27 for details of the timetable for the repeal/revocation of these provisions

Existing legislation	Key provisions to be replaced by PUWER*	Key provisions to be replaced by other legislation	Notes	What provisions of PUWER are particularly relevant?
The Offshore Installations (Construction and Survey) Regulations 1974				5, 11, 14, 20, 21
The Operations at Unfenced Machinery Regulations 1938	All			11
The Personal Protective Equipment at Work Regulations 1992			Implements Article 118A Directive	ALL
The Power Presses Regulations 1965				5, 6, 8, 9, 10, 11, 12, 23, 24
The Pressure Systems and Transportable Gas Containers Regulations 1989				5, 6, 10, 12, 13, 23, 24
The Shipbuilding and Ship-Repairing Regulations 1960	67	73,74		5, 11, 12
The Spinning by Self-Acting Mules Regulations 1905	All			5, 8, 9, 10, 11
The Factories (Testing of Aircraft Engines and Accessories) Regulations 1952				5, 12, 14-17
The Workplace (Health, Safety and Welfare) Regulations 1992			Implements Article 118A Directive	ALL, especially 6, 21
The Woodworking Machines Regulations 1974	1(2)+(3), 3(2), 5-9, 14-19, 21-38, 40-43	10-12	13 (Training), 20, 39 and Schedule 1 will remain	ALL

55

* See guidance under Regulations 1 and 27 for details of the timetable for the repeal/revocation of these provisions

Appendix 3

Further guidance on regulation 11 - dangerous parts of machinery

Explanation of safeguarding terms, regulation 11(2)

1   **Guards** are physical barriers which prevent access to the danger zone. **Fixed guards** have no moving parts and are fastened in a constant position relative to the danger zone (see Figure 4). They will normally need tools to undo the fasteners and remove them. If by themselves, or in conjunction with the structure of the equipment, they **enclose** the dangerous parts, fixed guards meet the requirements of the first level of the hierarchy. Note that it is permitted to have openings in fixed enclosing guards, and other types of guard, provided that they comply with appropriate safe reach distances (see EN 294).

2   **Other guards** in regulation 11(2)(b) include movable guards, adjustable guards, automatic guards and fixed guards that are not fully enclosing. **Movable guards** are likely to have interlocking. A control guard is a particular type of interlocked guard which should be used only in certain situations (see BS 5304). These allow limited access through openings, gates etc for feeding materials, making adjustments, cleaning, etc (see Figure 5).

3   **Protection devices** are devices which do not prevent access to the danger zone but stop the movement of the dangerous part before contact is made. Typical examples are mechanical trip devices, photoelectric devices (see Figure 6), pressure-sensitive mats and two-hand controls.

4   **Protection appliances** are used to hold or manipulate in a way which allows operators to control and feed a loose workpiece at a machine while keeping their body clear of the danger zone. They are commonly used in conjunction with woodworking machines (see Figure 7) and some other machines such as bandsaws for cutting meat. These appliances will normally be used in addition to guards.

5   Adequate **information, instruction, training and supervision** is always important, even if the hazard is protected by hardware measures. But they are especially important when the risk cannot be adequately eliminated by the hardware measures in regulation 11(2)(a) to (c). It may be necessary to lay down procedures to define what information, instruction, training and supervision must be given, and to restrict use of the equipment to those who have received it.

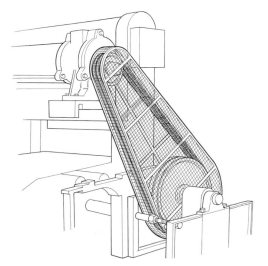

Figure 4 Fixed enclosing guard

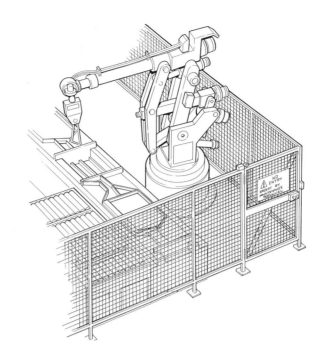

Figure 5 Perimeter fence guard with fixed panels and interlocking access door

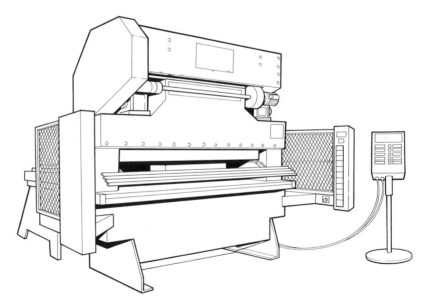

Figure 6 Photoelectric device fitted to a pressbrake

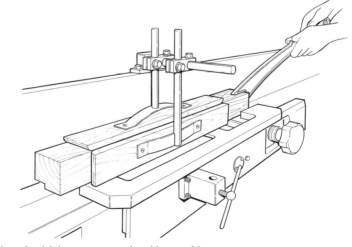

Figure 7 A push stick in use at a woodworking machine

Selection of measures

6   The guidance outlines how the hierarchy in regulation 11(2) should be applied in selecting safeguarding measures. Within each level of the hierarchy, there may be some choice available. In particular, the second level in the hierarchy allows a choice from among a number of different types of guard or protection device.

7   Regulation 11(2)(b) requires that when it is not practicable to use fixed enclosing guards, either at all or to the extent required for adequate protection, other guards and/or protection devices shall be used as far as practicable. One example is where the need for frequent access prevents the use of a fixed guard. In this situation it may be necessary to choose between an interlocked movable guard or a protection device. The foreseeable probability and severity of injury will influence the choice of measures from among the range of guards and protection devices that are available. Regulation 11(3)(a) requires that these must be suitable for their purpose. It is likely that some fixed guards will be practicable, and necessary to ensure that access can only be made through the movable opening guard or protection device. The use of movable guards which are interlocked is well established. Protection devices need to be carefully applied, taking into account the particular circumstances and the consequences of their failing to act as required.

8   Fixed distance guards, adjustable guards and other guards which do not completely enclose the dangerous parts should only be used in situations where it is not practicable to use fixed enclosing guards or protection devices which would give a greater level of protection.

Features of guards and protection devices, regulation 11(3)

Regulation 11(3)(a)

9   All guards and protection devices provided must be suitable for their purpose. In deciding what is suitable, employers should be guided by published national and international standards (see the reference section), guidance from HSC, HSE and industry associations, normal industrial practice and their own knowledge of the particular circumstances in which the machine is to be used.

10   A protection device or an interlocking system should be designed so that it will only operate as intended. Furthermore, if a component deteriorates or fails, the device or system should as far as possible fail in a safe manner by inhibiting the dangerous action of the machine. The force of this requirement depends on the combination of probability of failure and severity of the injury should the system fail. If the overall risk is high, then there should be adequate provision to counteract the effects of failure. Guidance on appropriate levels of protection is given in the publications referred to in paragraph 9.

Regulation 11(3)(b)

11   Guards and protection devices must be of good construction, sound material and adequate strength. They must be capable of doing the job they are intended to do. Several factors can be considered:

(a)   material of construction (metal, plastic, glass, etc);

(b)   form of the material (sheet, open mesh, bars, etc);

(c)   method of fixing.

12   Good construction involves design and layout as well the mechanical nature and quality of the construction. Foreseeable use and misuse should be taken into account.

Regulation 11(3)(c)

13   Guards and protection devices must be maintained in an efficient state, in efficient working order and in good repair. This is an important requirement as many accidents have occurred when guards have not been maintained. It is a particular example of the general requirement under regulation 6 to maintain equipment. Compliance can be achieved by the use of an effective inspection or checking procedure for guards and protection devices, together with any necessary follow-up action. In the case of protection devices or interlocks, some form of recorded functional check or test is desirable.

14   In the case of certain types of guards and protection devices, for example power press guarding in a factory, employers are required to comply with other legislation relating to testing and examination of the guards and protection devices and to keep records. Compliance with such additional legislation will not necessarily guarantee compliance with the duty to ensure guards and protection devices are maintained within the terms of this Regulation. Risk assessment will determine extra steps that are needed to ensure continuing integrity.

Regulation 11(3)(d)

15   Guards and protection devices must not themselves give rise to any increased risk to health or safety. One effect of this sub-paragraph is to prevent use of inherently hazardous measures for guarding.

16   A second effect is that guards must be constructed so that they are not themselves dangerous parts. If a guard is power operated or assisted, the closing or opening action might create a potentially dangerous trap which needs secondary protection, for example a leading-edge trip bar or pressure-sensitive strip.

17   The main concern is the overall effect on risk. The fact that a guard may itself present a minor risk should not rule out its use if it can protect against the risk of major injury. For example, sweep-away guards or manually-actuated sliding access gates might be able to cause minor injury, but their use in guarding against more serious risks is justified.

Regulation 11(3)(e)

18   Guards and protection devices must be designed and installed so that they can not be easily bypassed or disabled. This refers to accidental or deliberate action that removes the protection offered. By regulation 11(3)(a), guards must be suitable for their purpose, and one consequence of this is that simple mechanical bypassing or disabling should not be possible.

19   Movable panels in guards giving access to dangerous parts or movable guards themselves will often need to be fitted with an interlocking device. This device must be designed and installed so that it is difficult or impossible to bypass or defeat. Guidance on the selection and design of interlocking devices is available from the sources listed in paragraph 9.

20   In some cases, bypassing is needed for a particular purpose such as maintenance. The risks arising in such circumstances must be carefully assessed. As far as possible, the risks should be reduced or eliminated by appropriate design of the machinery - see regulation 22.

Regulation 11(3)(f)

21   Guards and protection devices must be situated at a sufficient distance from the danger zone they are protecting. In the case of solid fixed enclosing guards, there is no minimum distance between guard and danger zone, except that required for good engineering design. However, the gap between a fence

type guard or protection device and machine should normally be sufficiently small to prevent anybody remaining in it without being detected; alternatively, the space between guard or protection device and machine should be monitored by a suitable presence sensing device.

22   Where guarding is provided with holes or gaps (for visibility, ventilation or weight reduction for example), or is not fully enclosing, the holes must be positioned or sized so that it prevents foreseeable access to the danger zone. Published national and international standards give guidance on suitable distances and opening sizes in different circumstances.

23   The positioning of protection devices which stop the dangerous part before access can be gained to its danger zone will be affected by both the characteristics of the device itself (response time) and those of the machine to which it is fitted (time needed to stop). In these circumstances the device must be positioned so that it meets published criteria for the performance of such a system. Refer to the relevant standards and guidance.

24   Safeguarding is normally attached to the machine, but the Regulation does not preclude the use of free-standing guards or protection devices. In such cases, the guards or protection devices must be fixed in an appropriate position relative to the machine.

Regulation 11(3)(g)

25   Guards and protection devices must not unduly restrict the view of the operating cycle of the machinery, where such a view is necessary. It is not usually necessary to be able to see all the machine; the part that needs to be seen is normally that which is acting directly on material or a workpiece.

26   Operations for which it is necessary to provide a view include those where the operator controls and feeds a loose workpiece at a machine. Examples include woodworking machines, and food slicers. Many of these operations involve the use of protection appliances.

27   If the machine process needs to be seen, but cannot be, there is a temptation for the operator to remove or disable guards or interlocks. In such cases, some view of the work may be considered necessary. Examples are a hopper feeding a screw conveyor, milling machines, and power presses.

28   In other cases it may be convenient but not absolutely necessary to see the entire operating cycle. The Regulation does not prohibit providing a view in these cases, but does not require it; an example is an industrial tumble drier.

29   Where an operation protected by guards needs to be seen, the guard should be provided with viewing slits or properly constructed panels, perhaps backed up by internal lighting, enabling the operator to see the operation. The arrangements to ensure visibility should not prevent the guarding from carrying out its proper function; but any restriction of view should be the minimum compatible with that. An example of a guard providing necessary vision is viewing slits provided in the top guard of a circular saw.

Regulation 11(3)(h)

30   Guards and protection devices must be constructed or adapted so that they allow operations necessary to fit or replace parts and for maintenance work, restricting access so that it is allowed only to the area where the work is to be carried out and, if possible, without having to dismantle the guard or protection device.

31   This Regulation applies to the design of guards or protection devices so as to reduce risks arising from some particular operations. Regulation 22 applies

to the design of equipment as a whole so that maintenance and similar operations can be carried out safely; this Regulation is restricted to machine safeguards.

32   The aim is to design the safeguards so that operations like fitting or changing parts or maintenance can be done with minimal risk. If risk assessment shows this is not already the case, it may be possible to adapt the safeguarding appropriately.

33   Ideally, the machine is designed so that operations can be done in an area without risk, for example by using remote adjustment or maintenance points. If the work has to be done in the enclosed or protected area, then the safeguarding should be designed to restrict access just to that part where the work is to be carried out. This may mean using a series of guards.

34   If possible, the guard or protection device should not have to be dismantled. This is because of the possibility that after re-assembly, the guard or device may not work to its original performance standard.

Regulation 11(4)

35   Protection appliances also need to be suitable for their application. Factors for consideration come under the same headings as those for guards and protection devices as in regulation 11(3). Many of these are commonsense matters. Their design, material, manufacture and maintenance should all be adequate for the job they do. They should allow the person to use them without having to get too close to the danger zone, and they should not block the view of the workpiece.

References and further information

The EC Use of Work Equipment Directive

Council Directive of 30 November 1989 concerning the minimum safety and health requirements for the use of work equipment by workers at work (second individual Directive within the meaning of Article 16(1) of Directive 89/391/EEC) (89/655/EEC)
Official Journal of the European Communities No L 393/13 of 30.12.89.
Available from HMSO.

HSE publications

HSE *Essentials of health and safety at work* HMSO 1990 ISBN 011 885445 3

For a complete listing of HSC/E publications, refer to: *Publications in Series* available free from:

HSE Information Centre
Broad Lane
SHEFFIELD S3 7HQ
Tel: 0742 892345
Fax: 0742 892333

In addition, the following subject catalogues are published by HSE:

Agriculture	Student's guide to legislation, guidance, films and forms
Asbestos	List of HSC/E and other publications and films
Chemical manufacturing industry	List of HSC/E references
Construction	List of HSC/E references
COSHH	List of HSC/E references
Docks	Subject catalogue
Drinks	List of HSC/E publications
Food industry	List of HSC/E and relevant industry publications
Further and Higher Education	List of HSC/E and other relevant publications and films
Local authorities	List of HSC/E publications
Medical and hygiene information	List of HSC/E references including legislation, guidance and leaflets
Mines and quarries	List of HSC/E publications
Nuclear publications	List of HSC/E publications
Offshore Technology Reports	List of HSC/E publications
Plastics, leather and footwear	List of HSC/E and relevant industry publications
Printing	List of HSC/E publications (in preparation)
Railways Inspectorate	List of HSC/E publications
Rubber	List of HSC/E publications
Schools	List of HSC/E publications
Textile	List of HSC/E publications
Woodworking	List of HSC/E publications

European and British Standards

BS 5304: 1988 Code of practice for Safety of machinery

The first European Standards in support of the EC Machinery Directive have been published and are listed below. Others with the prefix 'pr' are provisional at the time of print:

BS EN 292: *Safety of machinery. Basic concepts, general principles for design* Parts 1 and 2:1991

BS EN 294:1992 *Safety of machinery. Safety distances to prevent danger zones being reached by the upper limbs*

BS EN 60204-1:1992 *Safety of machinery. Electrical equipment of machines. Part 1 General requirements*

prEN 349 *Safety of machinery. Minimum distances to avoid crushing of parts of the human body*

prEN 418: *Safety of machinery. Emergency stop equipment functional aspects. Principles for design*

prEN 811: *Safety of machinery. Safety distances to prevent danger zones being reached by the lower limbs*

prEN 50099: *Safety of machinery. Indicating, marking and actuating principles*

prEN 50100-1 *Safety of machinery. Electro-sensitive protective devices. Part 1 Specification for general requirements*

Other planned standards in support of the Machinery Directive covering specific safety devices, ergonomic aspects, etc include:

Risk assessment
Hand/arm speed (positioning of safety devices)
Guards, fixed and movable
Interlocking devices with and without guard locking
Electro-sensitive safety systems
Two-hand controls
Pressure sensitive protective devices, mats and floors
Pressure sensitive protective devices, edges and bars
Safety hold, isolation and energy dissipation
General principles for the design of safe control systems
Static electricity
Protocol for measuring radiation emitted by machinery
Fire and explosion
Safety requirements for fluid power systems and components
Anthropometric data
Principles for ergonomic design
Surface temperatures
Controls and signals
Visual displays
Integral lighting for machines
Safety symbols
Optical/acoustic signals

European and British Standards are available from British Standards Institution, Sales Department, Linford Wood, Milton Keynes MK14 6LE.

Printed in the United Kingdom for HSE, published by HMSO

C350   12/92